YOU'RE NOT THAT GREAT

YOU'RE NOT THAT GREAT

Daniel Crosby Ph.D.

WORD ASSOCIATION PUBLISHERS
www.wordassociation.com
1.800.827.7903

ISBN: 978-1-59571-834-1

Library of Congress Control Number: 2012920256

Designed and published by

Word Association Publishers

205 Fifth Avenue

Tarentum, Pennsylvania 15084

www.wordassociation.com

1.800.827.7903

Contents

INTRODUCTION

Naming me was my parents' first big fight. My mom and dad, both equally obstinate, were adamant about the special names each had chosen for their son. My mother was strongly of the opinion that I should be named "Charles" – a tribute to her father, an engineer and successful small business owner. My father on the other hand favored "Daniel" – homage to the Biblical prophet noted for his interpretation of dreams and stalwart adherence to his faith in the face of opposition (and lions!). As stubbornness gave way to excitement about my pending arrival, my parents settled on a compromise; they would name me Charles and call me Daniel, my middle name.

Although their mutual insistence shows that my parents understood the importance of names, they could scarcely have imagined how perfect my names have turned out to be. Although I was due on Halloween, I was born fifteen days early, on October 16, the two-year anniversary of my grandfather Charles's passing. What's more, I resemble my grandpa in a way that borders on unsettling – we are nearly indistinguishable from one another, a truth that my nana keeps top of mind. And what of my middle name, Daniel? Much like that Biblical prophet, I have chosen a profession that (at least historically) has placed a premium on the content of dreams. Also like Daniel, I routinely counsel with leaders – trying to help them navigate life's complexities in a way that benefits those they lead.

As much as I love my names, they have given me some trouble over the years. Naming your child one thing and calling him another is a surefire way to befuddle airline ticket counter attendants and all manner of bureaucrats. I haven't always loved my first name either. There was a time when "Charles" sounded to my young Southern ears like some overweight Briton, and I was ashamed when I was discovered as being thusly named. As I've outgrown those insecurities, being named after my grandfather has proven to profoundly shape how I think about the world.

Being named after a deceased relative who died on your birthday has a sobering effect on a person. Owing to our similar appearance and personalities, I've always felt a deep connection to my grandfather, although we never met. As a result of this felt closeness, I've always had an acute sense that not everyone gets the eighty or so years they assume they'll have. After all, my grandfather died when he was forty-three, leaving behind a wife and three children. This realization of the brevity of life and the suddenness with which it can be taken from us is not some morbid fascination on my part. Rather, it pushes me forward, encouraging me to take advantage of each moment, realizing that nothing is guaranteed.

As a result of this awareness, I've become obsessed with rules for living a good life and doing so from an early age. The book you're about to read contains some of those rules for successful living, put forth in a direct, sometimes irreverent manner. My purpose in using this rhetorical style is to reach people like me. People who want to live a good life, people who care about self-development, but who cannot stomach the saccharine way in which we typically have these conversations. What you're about to learn will be more of a punch in the face than a pat on the back, but I wouldn't have it any other way. After all, you only get one life (of indeterminate length) and the greatest sin of all is living it in a self-deluded way that keeps it from being as meaningful as it could be. So wake up! I'm not that great and neither are you, but we can begin to live in ways that make us uncomfortable in the best way possible.

CHAPTER ONE

YOU'RE NOT THAT GREAT

You're not that great.

Yes, you read that right. Wait a minute, you think, "This must be about that extra 15 pounds I'm carrying around." Nope. "Well, maybe it's because I always seem to quit on my New Year's resolutions in the first two weeks." Wrong again. "Wait a minute, how does he know about the time I swore at my teacher under my breath?!" I wish it were that insignificant a problem.

No, the reason you're not great is something that goes much deeper than all the sins of commission you could recall. Your problem is far more pervasive. Your problem is one that you're less aware of and is far more insidious than anything you've ever consciously done. Your problem is one you likely never even knew you had. We'll get back to your problem later in this chapter, but let's take a moment to talk about what it means to be great.

GREAT INFLATION

Soren Kierkegaard's "Attack Upon Christendom" is not an attack on his beloved Christianity per se, but rather an indictment of how the Church of Denmark had diluted and trivialized what it meant to be a Christian. [1]

According to Kierkegaard, the State's approach to institutional worship had commoditized faith and done damage to what he felt was true religion – an intimate, personal relationship with Deity.

By his reckoning, large congregations kept individuals from taking personal responsibility. Furthermore, the State's push for ever greater numbers of congregants and increased control of their personal lives made church more of a social than a religious institution and co-opted Christian symbols toward secular ends.

Another criticism of Kierkegaard's was that people had begun to identify themselves as Christian "as a matter of course." Gone was the struggle and danger of being thusly labeled – it had become a meaningless marker that carried the same weight as being left-handed or red headed.

Kierkegaard thought of this new brand of Christianity as a fake; while it had many of the trappings of religious worship, it was inwardly soulless and counterfeit. In the Biblical parlance, they drew near with their lips but their hearts were far away.

I believe that a similar dynamic is underfoot today in the world of "greatness." Leadership is the most studied of all psychological phenomena – a reality that puzzles researchers of more quotidian behaviors. After all, we experience happiness, sadness, frustration and humor with greater frequency than we do acts of great leadership, but none of these phenomena have captured our attention in quite the same way.

I believe this owes to the fact that some part of us believes that we can be special, even if our current behaviors and station may do little to suggest that latent potential. Quite simply, we believe that greatness is our birthright. And while this optimism about our own potential has real merit; feeling entitled to greatness has more damaging effects.

Atlas Shrugged[11] is a book beloved by college freshman the world over. Despite her less-than-stellar chops as a philosopher, Ayn Rand's work continues to influence everything from literary theory to political decision-making. Indeed, many of the architects of the disastrous economic policies of the last few years (Allan Greenspan notably) have cited Rand's ideas about personal uniqueness as underpinning their approach to economic policy.

Why is this? Because we identify with the story's protagonists and feel that we would certainly be on John Galt's short list. We dream of a civilization that appropriately teases out and honors the truly great, for surely we would be among the invited guests.

This is not so different from the tendency of the underprivileged to vote against social programs that would benefit them. They anticipate one day being rich, and in so doing, vote to protect those that already are. Similarly, we long to be exceptional and in that longing, tend to see exceptionality everywhere.

We have spread greatness too thinly. We have cheapened the term by coronating others too easily and by taking the mantle upon ourselves too lightly. If personal excellence is worth having, and it is, it must be struggled for, sought intentionally and hard won.

Remember, if everything that you do is an extraordinary act – nothing is.

GREATNESS – BORN OR MADE?

To ensure no misunderstanding about the above points, let me clarify that I don't believe greatness to be the birthright of the select few, nor do I think that by many people being great, we cheapen its value.

Quite the contrary, I preach that personal excellence can be taught and I do believe that it is available to people in all walks of life. What I am saying is that the solipsistic notion that greatness is our due, without the accompanying hard work, must go.

As a leadership coach, I am frequently asked whether leaders are born or made. It's a simple enough question but one that has huge implications for the way organizations and individuals set about the process of people development. After all, the very existence of coaching and development programs (and books like this) assumes that people can positively impact their performance through education and conscious choice. Otherwise, organizations should work to hire and identify exceptional talent but should pay no mind to further developing them once on board. Individuals hoping to improve themselves on the other hand would be largely out of luck.

America is a land of fanatical dedication to those we view as great men and women. We etch our Presidents' faces into the sides of mountains and engrave their likenesses on our currency. We pay leaders in the sports arena triple digit multiples of what the rest of us make and look to them for moral guidance, often with disappointing results. Business leaders like Bill Gates, Warren Buffet, and Steve Jobs become household names whose behaviors are studied and become "best practices" post hoc. Our glorification of these leaders, while problematic in some respects, rests on the assumption that they have lived their lives and made choices that are extraordinary and that they should be recognized thusly. But would they deserve the same praise if they had been "born that way?"

GREATNESS, CHOICE AND MEANING

On her second birthday, I took my daughter to Build-A-Bear to well, you know, build a bear. After choosing her panda ("This panda loves me daddy!"), we began the process of stuffing and eventually sewing up the little plush toy. As part of the process, she placed a small felt heart and a recorded message inside that says, "I love you" when you depress the bear's stomach.

Now, I can press Panda's stomach and hear those three little words whenever I'd like. I know that without a doubt, if I press her stomach, she will tell me that she loves me – she was born that way. My daughter also tells me that she loves me, but is far less consistent in how she goes about it. In fact, in addition to her frequent expressions of love, she has also told me on occasion that I smell bad, have a pimple, and that she does not like me. So, if the words are the same coming from either source, why does it warm my heart when it comes from my little girl and mean nothing from a bear? The thing that makes action meaningful is that it is chosen from a host of other, often opposite, choices.

CHOOSING GREATNESS

Viktor Frankl, Holocaust survivor and renowned Austrian psychiatrist said it best, "Between stimulus and response there is a space. In that space is our power to choose our response. In that response lies our growth and freedom."[III] Some may say that the best and brightest are born; that they come into the world with everything they need to be great. If that is the case, I see nothing laudable about greatness. They are simply living out their destiny in much the same way that Panda is, doing what they were programmed to do.

I think that true personal greatness is made. I think that there is a leader within each of us, and that we can all be great in our own sphere. I also think that we can choose to be lazy, bigoted, hateful, and thwart our growth through our own indifference. That we are capable of both great leadership and great waste is what makes choosing to be great so very special.

SELF HELP HELPS ITSELF

Psychologists, leadership gurus and televangelists are among the myriad talking heads that have benefitted from "great inflation" and the notion that greatness is our due. After all, what could be easier to sell than the message that wealth, fame and giftedness are rights to be had, not privileges to be earned? We have been flattered by those looking to sell a book or pass a collection plate and flattery has gotten them everywhere. Simply put, flattery of this sort moves units but it does not change lives. Consider the following:

International bestseller *The Secret* states that desirable outcomes such as health and wealth can be attracted simply by changing thoughts and feelings. For instance, if a person wanted a new boat, by thinking about the boat, having thankful feelings about the boat as if it were already attained and opening one's life for a new boat to be acquired (e.g., looking at boats online) the law of attraction would rearrange events to make it possible for the boat to appear in the person's life.

Despite the gross overstatements and illogic of *The Secret*, the video and attendant book have flourished. After being featured twice on The Oprah Winfrey Show, the book has eventually gone on to sell over 21 million copies and be translated into 44 languages. Spinoffs are currently underway for a similar series aimed at bringing the message of *The Secret* to teens.[IV]

Similarly, televangelists who preach "prosperity theology" (the idea that God wishes for the faithful to be wealthy) have been able to amass great personal wealth on the backs of their largely low-socio-economic-status viewership.

The psychology behind this approach is common-sensical and compelling; we are loathe to turn down a compliment. When someone tells us that God wishes for us to own a yacht or that we can attain one simply by willing it to be so, who are we to frown upon something so inviting? The people who make their living by this kind of flattery understand this. They tell us what we want to hear, and in a world where we are bombarded with bad news at every turn, we let them lie to us. Leapfrogging logic, we settle into these comfortable half-truths and begin to start living accordingly.

The problem ultimately arises when the disingenuousness of these statements becomes apparent in our lives. We want to believe that we can have a meaningful life without any extraordinary effort on our part, but we sense deep down that it doesn't really work that way. Like the counterfeit religion of Kierkegaard's day, this dumbed down approach to living the good life never quite sates our appetite. As much as we want to believe we can be great without really trying, we still feel empty. An emptiness, that if we're not careful, can put us right back where we started – lying to ourselves and letting others lie to us about what it takes to lead a special life in order to soothe our troubled mind.

MY PROMISE

I am commonly called upon to speak to teams of executives about what it takes to deliver effective feedback to their peers and subordinates. This is a topic of much consternation among businesspeople as "feedback" is often seen as little more than a euphemism for micro-management and passive-aggressive sniping. Attempting to simplify a concept that has become grossly over-complicated, I offer one piece of advice about feedback that underpins all of my additional comments. I advise all of my clients to consider one simple statement, "Does the feedback make him or her look good?"

To explain using a silly example, consider dining with a close friend who has chosen the healthy route and ordered a salad for lunch. At some point, a piece of spinach becomes lodged in her teeth and is visible as she continues to talk. You are faced with a conundrum – do you mention the wayward green to your friend or do you allow her to go about her business?

Let's consider your options in light of the mandate to "make her look good." If you remain silent, you avoid an awkward conversation and you go about your lunch unperturbed. However, she is likely to have meetings and interactions with people later in the day with whom she is less close. This being the case, she is made to look bad in front of people who might judge her more superficially than you. Your decision to remain silent is ultimately more about you looking good (and avoiding an awkward conversation) than making her look good.

If you choose to speak up on the other hand, you sacrifice a moment of personal discomfort (no one likes to be the bearer of bad news after all!) for the greater good of your friend. While she might have liked to go on blissfully about her conversation, the fact was that she had an embarrassing thing stuck in her teeth that was going to impact the way in which she interacted with others. Ultimately, if you choose the latter course of action, you are the superior friend in that you put your own displeasure with awkward conversations behind your desire to make your friend appear like the confident, competent person she truly is.

So, to further torture this analogy, I promise that this book will tell you every time that you have spinach in your teeth. It would be easier and indubitably more profitable to sell you on yet another get-rich-quick scheme or to ply you with all of the reasons why what you are currently doing is exactly what you need to be doing. Fortunately or unfortunately though, I like you and I do want you to look good, which means that we need to talk.

WHAT'S YOUR PROBLEM?

At the beginning of this chapter I intimated that you have a problem, and you do. Your problem is not that you've done something wrong intentionally, it's that you don't always realize the ways in which you are on autopilot. It's not that you're living a bad life, it's more that life is living you. The purpose of this book is to shine a light into some of the forgotten corners of your life. To bring you face to face with the subtle, reflexive and even unconscious things you do to sabotage yourself. Remember, just because you are not aware of something does not mean it does not have a negative impact on your quality of life. In fact, the things we'll discuss within are especially damaging inasmuch as you are unaware of them. By illuminating these errors in thinking and behaving, you'll be better equipped to live an intentional life and feel more in control.

MIT researcher and father of artificial intelligence Marvin Minsky said it best, "In general, we are least aware of what our minds do best."[V] We are not aware of the ways in which we are selling ourselves short because they have become almost second nature to us! As you'll learn in the following pages, one of the things our minds do best is preserve the status quo and protect mediocrity. Our reptile brain, the one that we default to, keeps us fed and safe, but doesn't make us great. Left to its own devices, the brain is programmed for survival, not exceptionality. However, we are also meaning-seeking creatures that, once we have met our basic needs, long for something much greater than just getting by. Unless we learn to recognize and break free of the deep grooves of banality that we have tread for ourselves, we will always find our lives lacking in some important, if ineffable way.

If you choose to continue reading, you will be brought face to face with some uncomfortable truths. You will squirm. You will feel implicated. You will recognize biases and illogical behaviors in yourself that have hurt you in the past. You may even get angry and wish you could go back to living life with blinders on. If you're not prepared for this, maybe you should put this book down and pick up something with a glossy cover and big letters on the front. Better yet, go watch TV.

But if you are ready to sit with that discomfort and the way to a better- vetted and more fulfilling life, read on. Because what follows promises to be as meaningful as it is hard to hear. As Socrates said, "The unexamined life is not worth living."[VI] And while you may not be that great today, greatness is within your grasp if you'll take back your life by taking a closer look.

CHAPTER TWO

YOU ARE NOT SPECIAL

America is a nation in love with giftedness. Sure, we applaud bootstrapped grit too but it isn't it a little more awe-inspiring when it is made to look easy? Watch any sporting event and you are sure to hear telecasters speaking in reverent tones about so-and-so athlete who seems to defy the laws of physics without even breaking a sweat. What must it be like, we ask ourselves, to be that good and not have to work for it?

Our infatuation turns to jealous anger when one of our idols reveals that they are not even a fan of the sport at which they are so highly gifted (and for which they are so well compensated). Andre Agassi and Serena Williams, two of the greatest tennis players of all time, have both admitted to not really loving the game that made them famous. In both cases, the public lashed out, incensed that someone so gifted could seemingly care so little. But at the end of the day, our vitriol toward them is just the flipside of the adoration coin; we love their talent and curse that it was not more justly distributed.

THE MYTH OF SELF-ESTEEM

Ever since the 1969 publication of *The Psychology of Self-Esteem* [VII], wherein Nathaniel Branden posited that self-esteem was the single most important facet of personal well being, the self-esteem movement has been one of far-reaching influence. In the 70s and 80s anything seen as detrimental to self-esteem was done away with. Gold stars proliferated while red pens gathered dust. First place trophies gave way to awards for participation. In this new milieu, everyone was a winner; everyone was special.

As this well-intentioned movement garnered support, scholarly research followed. In the thirty-year run up to the 21st century, over 15,000 articles were written on the impact of self-esteem on, well, pretty much everything imaginable. However, the results of these myriad studies were often confusing or inconclusive. In an attempt to make sense of the general trajectory of the literature on self-esteem, the Association for Psychological Science asked Dr. Roy Baumeister, an admitted proponent of the theory, to meta-analyze the extant data on the subject. What followed was what Dr. Baumeister would go on to refer to as "the biggest disappointment of my career."

Of the 15,000 studies taken into consideration, a paltry .013 percent of them (n = 200) met the more rigorous standards for inclusion into the meta-analysis.[VIII] To begin with, it became apparent that many of the theories about self-esteem that had impacted policy were simply junk science. What's more, the studies that did pass muster didn't have much good to say about the construct's predictive power. Self-esteem did not predict academic or career achievement, nor did it predict drug usage or violent aggression. The biggest finding to emerge from the self-esteem movement was that praise did not predict self-esteem, accomplishment did. Telling someone that they are special is insufficient if they have not worked to earn it. We have an accurate internal sense of when we have earned praise and when we have not. If we feel as though we are being patted on the back undeservingly, it does not move the self-esteem needle one inch.

So, our obsession with widespread specialness doesn't predict much, but surely it's not damaging right? Wrong. Our wish, no, need to be special has at least three negative sequelae – it leads us to give up easily, act unethically and mistreat others.

SPECIAL PEOPLE ARE QUITTERS

Dmitri Martin, one of my favorite comedians, is known for his humorous sketches, delivered deadpan, that speak to harsh truths with which we are all well acquainted. One such sketch is the one where he compares most peoples' concept of the path to success with the actuality of the path to success.

Most of us know intellectually that hard work and failure often precede success. We probably even have a couple of go to anecdotes (that do little to make us feel better about our own shortcomings, incidentally) – Michael Jordan was cut from his high school basketball team, Thomas Edison failed thousands of times before inventing a commercially viable light bulb filament. But, however much we may wish it were different, success is typically preceded by a good deal of imperfection and those who go on to do great things are the ones who learn to fight through.

So, what does a feeling of personal specialness have to do with stick-to-it-ive-ness? A great deal as it turns out. Carol Dweck and her team have pioneered the research in this field in the trenches of the New York City school system. Dweck's team took a random sample of children out of their fifth grade classes, and in the first round of the experiment, provided them with puzzles simple enough that most children could excel. To the first group of children, she complimented their intelligence, "You did well, you must be very smart." To the second group, she complimented their effort, "You did well, you must have worked very hard."

For the second round of the test, the children were given an option. They could choose a harder test or a test equivalently hard to the first. Of those praised for hard work, 90% opted for the harder option, whereas a majority of those praised for intelligence opted to stay with the easier test.[IX]

It seems that people who believe that they are naturally gifted tend to quit earlier and choose simpler tasks than those who have been socialized to work hard. Feeling special produces a euphoric high that people are understandably hesitant to part with. Thus, when special people are confronted with an especially difficult task, they often back down, seeing it as a threat to their "crown of giftedness." After all, why risk the possibility of failure when you could bask in the safety of "specialness?"

Many a doting parent has sought to buoy the self-esteem of their little darling by telling their son or daughter that they are smart. After all, it stands to reason that intelligent people are more successful and in the case of girls, it circumvents the sexist habit of focusing solely on attractiveness. But thirty years of research tells us that focusing on effort rather than specialness is the best way to encourage young Einsteins.

Dr. Dweck relates the story of "Jonathan" (a composite character) in her seminal article, *The Secret To Raising Smart Kids*.[X]

"A brilliant student, Jonathan sailed through grade school. He completed his assignments easily and routinely earned As.

Jonathan puzzled over why some of his classmates struggled, and his parents told him he had a special gift. In the seventh grade, however, Jonathan suddenly lost interest in school, refusing to do homework or study for tests. As a consequence, his grades plummeted. His parents tried to boost their son's confidence by assuring him that he was very smart. But their attempts failed to motivate Jonathan. Schoolwork, their son maintained, was boring and pointless."

What many a well-meaning parent has done when emphasizing innate gifts is create the perception that achievement is based on leveraging specialness rather than hard work. When children view themselves as special or gifted, they become accustomed and entitled to having work come easily to them. When it does not, they write it off as "stupid" or "boring." Worse still, they believe themselves to be ineffectual in doing differently, since after all, their past ability to excel has all been predicated on natural gifts they did nothing to earn.

This mindset is doubly damning. When a child is successful, they are unable to truly take credit for their success, since it is a natural consequence of their unearned gift. When they are unsuccessful, they have no culpability and could not have done any better, since success is contingent upon a talent with which they were not blessed. This "either 'ya got it or 'ya don't" attitude leads to something that psychologists call "learned helplessness."

LEARNED HELPLESSNESS

The original research on learned helplessness was conducted by one of the fathers of positive psychology, Martin Seligman.[XI] Dr. Seligman's experiment tested two groups of dogs. The first set of dogs were harnessed in and given a mild electrical shock which could end by pressing a lever inside of their cage. Soon enough, the dogs stumbled onto the correct response and learned to act in every instance of discomfort. The second set of dogs were similarly harnessed and shocked, but were initially unable to bring about the cessation of shock by pressing the lever. After repeated pairings with this helpless situation, they were then placed in new cages where their action could bring about the end of the shock by pressing the lever. Sadly, by this time, the dogs had conditioned themselves to helplessness and directed their energy toward enduring the pain rather than improving their plight.

It is easy to draw parallels between the helplessness of the dogs and a student who has bought into the notion that success is predicated entirely on innate specialness. After all, his success and failure is seen as being entirely out of his hands – so why try? Given the unintended consequences of praising children as special, Dweck and other experts on giftedness encourage taking a different tact. Rather than praising giftedness, they recommend praising hard work and encouraging a growth mentality. In so doing, children learn that they will be praised for process rather than outcomes. This approach empowers young minds and teaches them success is in fact a byproduct of effort and that whatever their natural gifts may (or may not) be, they can bring about improved outcomes with sweat equity.

THE ETHICS OF GIFTEDNESS

One of the thoughts behind the self-esteem movement was, that if you imbued people with a positive vision of themselves, they would be less likely to engage in anti-social behavior. Once again, the reality of specialness deviates quickly from the aspirational theory that underlies it. In fact, research shows that those who think of themselves as gifted, will often do anything to protect that label – even if it is unethical.

One of the most direct studies of this phenomenon involves students who were asked to fill out a "do it yourself" report card that would ostensibly be mailed to students at another school. The children involved were told that those on the receiving end of these report cards would be strangers – they would never meet them nor would they exchange names. By setting up the experiment thusly, the researchers were able to promote a scenario that would allow the children to lie with impunity, if they so chose.

Before filling out the DIY report cards, the kids were either praised for their effort or for being naturally intelligent. While very few of those praised for effort dissimulated on the grades self-assessment, 40% of those lauded for their specialness lied in their self-reports of academic achievement. Again, the shroud of specialness created a pleasant illusion that the students wanted to perpetuate at all costs. Whereas being complimented for being hard working has a wholesomeness that is it's own reward, specialness is something that is won or lost in the outcomes. The impact of dishonesty is bad enough, but what if this dynamic played out on a grander stage and with infinitely higher stakes?

"A LITTLE JEWISH GUY FROM BROOKLYN"

By now we are all familiar with the story of Bernie Madoff, the financier who brokered the largest Ponzi Scheme in US history. In the case of Madoff, our familiarity with the story may actually be a disservice to an appropriate understanding of his motives. After all, in the minds of "have nots", wealth is its own reward. Who wouldn't want a private jet? Who wouldn't want a $200,000 watch? We assume a very simplistic motive on Madoff's part – greed. But the reality may not be that simple.

While the timeline for Madoff's transition from legitimate businessman to crook is unclear, it appears as though he began his career on the up and up. In fact, Madoff's firm legitimately pioneered the use of computer information to disseminate stock quotes. This technology was so groundbreaking, that after some initial testing it become what we now know as NASDAQ. Despite all of his success, Madoff felt unnoticed and unextraordinary saying, "I was upset at the whole idea of not being in the (Wall Street insiders) club. I was this little Jewish guy from Brooklyn."XII For someone who had done so much and went on to cause such trouble, Madoff sounds weak and vulnerable in his account of his early career.

Much like a professional athlete who turns to "juicing" to rise to the top, Madoff began to apply his financial acumen in a more sinister manner, officially defrauding his investors (which included Holocaust survivor charities) of over $18 billion. But as he has said in interviews, it really was never about the money. Said Madoff, "We made a very nice living. I didn't need the investment-advisory business. I took it on and got myself involved in it, but if you think I woke up one morning and said, 'Well, listen, I need to be able to buy a boat and a plane, and this is what I'm going to do,' that's wrong."XIII Madoff's subtext? It was never about the money, it was about respect.

Before long, Madoff's too good to be true returns did result in the recognition he craved. "The chairman of Banco Santander came down to see me, the chairman of Credit Suisse came down, the chairman of UBS came down; I had all of these major banks" he says, "It is a head trip. (Those people) sitting there, telling you, 'You can do this.' It feeds your ego. All of a sudden, these banks which wouldn't give you the time of day, they're willing to give you a billion dollars." Now Madoff was special, but as we have seen, with recognition comes the tenuous task of maintaining the label. Madoff was now a prisoner of his own need to be recognized. He said of living this lie, "It was a nightmare for me. I wish they caught me six years ago. Eight years ago." Even in the face of this torment, he was unable to free himself from his need to be thought of highly by his peers, the Wall Street insiders who had never really accepted the Jewish kid from Brooklyn as one of their own.

SPECIALNESS AND THE OTHER

We have seen how the need to be special leads us to disengage from life and bend the rules, but how does it impact our interaction with the people around us? We can begin to answer this question as we examine how we measure specialness in the first place. As we attempt to measure the good life, we are immediately presented with this difficulty – there is no objective measure of what constitutes specialness. Sure, we have approximations: wealth, position, power, relationships, sex, and other status symbols, but all of these are imperfect measures. We are further handicapped by not being able to compare our life, apples to apples, with every person everywhere and at all times throughout history. Given these encumbrances to measuring specialness, we tend to measure it in relative terms and look to our neighbors to size up our own worth.

Compared to those who lived 500 years ago, the average American enjoys untold privilege that scarcely register as special to our spoiled modern minds. Air conditioning, automobiles, fresh food from across the globe available at low cost, are just a few easy examples of modern conveniences that would have been the stuff of science fiction not all that many years ago. Similarly, even low socioeconomic status Westerners enjoy access to food and medicine that would seems lavish by the standards of Sub-

Saharan Africa. But, our notion of specialness is relational and relative, which means that many in our land of plenty perceive a substantial degree of want.

This juxtaposition of our own goodness relative to that of our neighbors is what psychologists call "contingent self-esteem." When operating under this mindset, we are presented with only two options if we hope to buoy our own feelings of self-worth. We can increase our own feelings of competence through accomplishment or we can diminish theirs. All too often, we choose the path of least resistance in this zero sum game and choose the latter.

WHAT CAN A TERMITE TEACH YOU ABOUT GIFTEDNESS?

The most comprehensive longitudinal study ever completed on the impact of giftedness was undertaken by Stanford psychologist Lewis Terman.[XIV] Dr. Terman was fascinated by genius and held a theory, that while brilliance was primarily inherited, it could be positively impacted by appropriate schooling. In an effort to determine how best to educate the exceptionally gifted, Terman designed a study he called "Genetic Studies of Genius" that followed a group of exceptionally gifted students and catalogued their activity over a lifetime. The participants in the study were affectionately referred to by a nickname - "Terman's Termites."

There was nothing average about the average Termite. With a mean IQ of 151, these gifted children were three and a half standard deviations north of the mean intelligence quotient of 100. One of Terman's obsessions was to prove that even the highly gifted were not the reclusive nerds they were so often portrayed to be. Indeed, thirty-five years out, his findings were notable in that they dispelled such notions about the very intelligent. Many of the Termites were as emotionally intelligent as they were smart, and had satisfying relationships. In addition, many of them had gone on to produce exceptional professional results. To quote Terman's findings:

"Nearly 2000 scientific and technical papers and articles and some 60 books and monographs in the sciences, literature, arts, and humanities have been published. Patents granted amount to at least 230. Other writings include 33 novels, about 375 short stories, novelettes, and plays; 60 or more essays, critiques, and sketches; and 265 miscellaneous articles on a variety of subjects. The figures on publications do not include the hundreds of publications by journalists that classify as news stories, editorials, or newspaper columns, nor do they include the hundreds, if not thousands, of radio, television, or motion picture scripts."

While Terman's findings did indeed support his notion that the naturally gifted often went on to greatness, there was also some disappointment that none of the participants had gone on to do anything world-changing.[xv] Their accomplishments had been laudable, sure, but relative to the expectations of this group of young savants, they still seemed a bit disappointing. Subsequent analysis of the Termites has shown that their level of success could have been predicted by socio-economic status alone, as this group was no more successful than their similarly upper middle class and wealthy peers. However, one young man affiliated with the study had gone on to change the world. His name was William Shockley.

Identified as potentially gifted early on, William Shockley was tested as part of Dr. Terman's research and found wanting. Shockley's IQ was deemed too low for inclusion in the study and he was labeled "not gifted." In spite, or perhaps because of this early labeling, Shockley went on to have an exceptional academic career, earning a Ph.D. from Harvard before securing a job with the legendary Bell Labs. While there, he developed two transistors that earned him a prize no less auspicious than the Nobel Peace Prize in Physics. He would eventually be named to the "100 Most Influential Thinkers of the 20th Century" by Time Magazine.[XVI]

William Shockley's story demonstrates how, despite our obsession with predicting giftedness, actual accomplishment is a far more complicated thing to measure than is raw talent. Stories like Shockley's are instructive inasmuch as they teach us the limits and dangers of foreclosing on students as "gifted" or "ungifted", especially at such a formative age. However, the lessons learned from this tale are hardly academic alone in nature - William Shockley's story also has a great deal to teach us about how specialness impacts the way we treat one another.

Snubbed as a youth, Shockley went on to have professional life that far exceeded the accomplishments of those supposedly more gifted than he. While it is impossible to know the precise impact of this on a young mind, it seems feasible that William had something to prove to the world. Having been hit so early by the stick of "not good enough", Shockley went on to wield that stick against others in much the same fashion following his own rise to prominence.

Later in his life, Shockley became fascinated with the study of race and genetics. He became an outspoken proponent of "eugenics" which derives from the prefix "eu" meaning good and "genics" as in genes. Quite literally, eugenics is the study of how to optimize the genetic composition of a human population. While there is nothing inherently wrong with the study of good genes, the study of eugenics often found itself ensnared in racist half truths and ultimately fell out of favor because of the eugenic experiments performed by Nazis in WWII. Shockley himself was worried that the black population, which was reproducing more quickly than whites, would begin to undo the gains made by the civil rights movement if those with low IQ's were allowed to reproduce.[XVII] He went on to advocate that those with an IQ less than 100 should be paid to be sterilized. Shockley's story illustrates how a man done an injustice by the cult of specialness could still not free himself of the intoxicating power of being "better than" once he had himself arrived. As his story clearly shows, this type of designation is reckless and pits brother against brother for the scarce resource of greatness. Shockley was hit early with the "not good enough stick", but once it was in his hands, he hit right back.

THE WAY FORWARD

For too long, we have prayed to the false god of specialness and have been "rewarded" with unethical, antisocial, and unfulfilling behavior. Greatness can and should be sought after, but not when our definition of it is moored in greed and doing ill to our fellow people. If greatness is worth pursuing, one person's success cannot be tantamount to another person's failure. If it were, then greatness could neither be created nor destroyed, and your pursuit of excellence would be simultaneously a quest to diminish someone else's quality of life. In order for greatness to be great, it must be effortful, ethical, and intraindividual.

Effortful – People are meant to work. This may seem counterintuitive at first blush, after all, isn't part of the point of being special that you don't have to work? Well, sort of. To explain, people are NOT meant to work like we currently do in the US. The 40 hour work week is a vestige of the Industrial

Age and has little to do with how the world works in the new knowledge economy. Even so, many a retiree has dreamed of lazy days on the golf course, only to find out that it gets old fast.

If the gold star self-esteem movement has taught us anything it is that you cannot self-deceive your way to feeling good about yourself. Legitimate feelings of self-worth result from effort. This is not some anachronistic rant about the good old days or building character, it's science. All too often, a focus on outcomes rather than effort leads to a Machiavellian approach where outcomes are justified by any means necessary. Many of the examples of misbehavior you read about above were brought to bear by people who focused on arriving at a destination without doing the appropriate legwork. By all means, be strategic, look for ways to be more productive, but realize that true greatness takes work if it is to last and be at all satisfying.

Ethical – Sometimes the games we play have so much to teach us about the bigger game of life. Consider baseball in the 80's and 90's – at the time dubbed the "Longball Era" and since nicknamed the "Steroid Era." Abuse of performance enhancing drugs was widespread and the commissioner and owners looked the other way as players began to mount eye-popping numbers while putting on otherworldly amounts of muscle mass. While it was a fun ride in the short term, the unethical acts of those drug abusers tainted those two decades for all who participated. As many of those suspected of abuse come up for inclusion in the Hall of Fame, voters wrestle to separate the truly gifted from the cheaters. Baseball, much like life, rests on a foundational assumption of fair play. When people engage in unethical behavior, it spoils it for all involved.

Reconsider Bernie Madoff's comments about wishing he had been caught years earlier. Cheating toward greatness does not sate our desire for self-worth in any meaningful way. Far from it, it simply deepens our view of ourselves as fraudulent and places us in a lose-lose situation. Even if others label us as special, we know the truth about our actions and internally discount their praise. Consider Barry Bonds, who by all rights was a preternaturally gifted athlete. His alleged drug use has obscured his true gift; blocking what would have surely been a Hall of Fame career otherwise. Add to this internal authenticity the fear and suspicion of being caught and it becomes easy to see how the unethical pursuit of excellence is an exercise in certain misery.

Intraindividual – In game theory, a zero sum game is one in which one participants gain of something is offset by an equivalent loss in another player. For far too long, we have viewed greatness as a zero sum game, where I am required to elevate myself over you, to dominate you in order to be successful myself. Leadership guru Stephen Covey refers to this as the "scarcity mentality" in his classic, "The Seven Habits of Highly Effective People." Says Covey of this mindset, "People with a scarcity mentality tend to see everything in terms of win-lose. There is only so much, and if someone else has it, that means there will be less for me. …the more we develop an abundance mentality, the more we are genuinely happy for the successes, well-being, achievements, recognition and good fortune of other people. We believe their success adds to, rather than detracts from, our lives."

As we long as we discuss excellence in relationally relative terms and try to keep up with the proverbial Joneses, antisocial behavior and the pursuit of specialness will go hand in hand. I propose a new standard for measuring greatness, one based on intraindividual rather than interdividual measurement. As Ernest Hemingway said more beautifully, "There is nothing noble in being superior to your fellowman; true nobility is in being superior to your former self."

Aside from the tendency to want to drag down others to create the illusion of our own success, interindividual comparison is problematic in that it is too subjective. Every one of us has a façade that we show the world that is somewhat more polished than the reality of internal experience. This is not dishonesty or subterfuge on our part, it is socially acceptable and appropriate. It is wise to not be entirely vulnerable with every person we meet, and we only have the capacity to truly open up to a few people in our lives.

I once sat down next to a woman on a plane and upon hearing that I was a psychologist, she opened up to me about a history of childhood abuse and neglect. While I treated her story with the appropriate circumspection and respect, it was nonetheless jarring to experience that degree of vulnerability without the appropriate relational foundation. The colloquial terms for this phenomenon are "TMI" (too much information) and "overshare."

Since the emotionally healthy among us do not share intimate details with the public, what does get shared can look a little bit like a highlight reel of our lives rather than a play-by-play. A recent study showed that people who spent a great deal of time on Facebook were more depressed than their peers who did not. The reason for this is that Facebook is little but a brag sheet where people boast about the good things happening in their lives, often omitting the sad or boring parts that happen every day. Being exposed to the best of what is going on with others and juxtaposing that with our intimate familiarity with every disappointing detail in our own lives is a recipe for feeling like a failure.

Interindividual comparison is a deck that is stacked against us, we know all of our own highs and lows, but tend to see mostly the highs of those with whom we are comparing ourselves. This being so, it makes sense that the most realistic barometer of our personal wellbeing lies in comparing the person we are today with the person we were yesterday. Human beings are infinitely complicated and the number of variables that contribute to our success or lack of success are too numerous to count. Those interested in truly measuring their personal progress need only look inward to determine where they sit on the path to greatness.

LIVED LEARNING CHALLENGE

★ Determine one area in your life wherein you compare yourself unfavorably with others. How might you increase your happiness and your ability to achieve if you started using yourself as your gauge of success?

★ Greatness is not accidental and doesn't happen with a great deal of hard work. What is one thing you could start doing today to start putting yourself on the road to the happiness borne of effort?

CHAPTER THREE

YOU'RE KIND OF CRAZY

I want you to take a moment and imagine your quirkiest, most idiosyncratic acquaintance. Perhaps it is a coworker whose tendency to break all the social conventions you hold most dear makes you scratch your head. Maybe it's a crazy aunt or uncle who nonplusses the relatives at each holiday gathering. It could even be a spouse or partner, who although you love them dearly, does things from time to time that make you question their sanity. Consider the most nonsensical thing they have ever done. Go on, imagine it, recount it in detail and puzzle at their downright weirdness. Now, I want you to realize that if we did this exercise with enough people, someone would be imagining YOU. That's right, you are someone's weird aunt or uncle.

The strange brew of nature and nurture that goes into making each one of us who we are means that inevitably there will be those that see our customs and worldview as plain old nuts. Sometimes this perceived craziness is a result of cultural differences as was the case when I (a man from Alabama) lived in the Philippines for two years. At one point during my two-year sojourn in the Southeast Asia, I was holding the new baby of a friend. As is the American custom, I was goo-goo-ga-gaing at the baby and telling her how pretty she was ("Aren't you the prettiest little baby? Aren't you? Aren't you?").

In an effort to corroborate my claims of her beauty, I held the baby up to the mirror so she could behold for herself her own adorableness ("Who's a pretty baby? You are! You are!"). My Filipino guests were shocked and immediately snatched the baby from my arms to my great surprise. New to the country, my Tagalog was still rusty and I was even more unfamiliar with local customs. Appalled at my behavior, my hosts asked, "Don't you know it's bad luck to show a baby it's reflection?!" Incensed, they asked me to leave for having so mistreated their child.

Over the next two years, I became aware of a number of Filipino customs not traditionally held by Americans (at least not those from the Deep South). When Filipinos have not heard you, they sit with their mouth agape until you repeat yourself. They believe that sweat drying on your neck leads to illness and therefore profusely powder their necks with talc and wear towels in the back of their shirts. They are of the mind that eating fruit quickly after rice will make you sick, and so on.

Likewise, Filipinos thought Americans were cruel and inhumane for placing the elderly in assisted living facilities. They also thought that the American cultural norm that a child should "fly the coop" at 18, never to return on a permanent basis was evidence that American families were less tight knit than their own. You see, "crazy" is largely a cultural phenomenon. What seems nuts to you may be perfectly acceptable to me and vice versa. And while the US and the Philippines are thousands of miles away, both physically and culturally, every person that you meet is a cultural microcosm with traditions and quirks all their own.

As with all behaviors, shrinks have come up with a fancy term to describe how a behavior can make sense to me but not to you.

The term for a thought, behavior or feeling that is consistent with one's idea of the good life is — egosyntonic. Conversely, one that is inconsistent with one's idea of the good life is termed — egodystonic. When I attended college in the Western US, I was legitimately unaware that the terms "used to could" and "fixin' to" were regionalisms. Everyone I knew used these terms and having traveled very little, their use was egosyntonic to me. However, when my use of these phrases came in contact with the similarly distinct culture of the West, the "weirdness" of it was made apparent to me. The reason that you are someone's "go to weirdo" is quite simply that you have been socialized to believe and act in ways different than their own socialization.

A SAD SILENCE

Work-Life balance. We are all familiar with the term and ostensibly its increased acceptance bodes well for those of us who value wellness and holism. But as is so often the case with language, the term itself accurately conveys the way we think of "work" and "life" as separate entities that should be managed, but never intersect. Work happens from 8 to 5, life happens before and after. You are one person at work, you are another in your free time. The implications of the term are clear, "Don't bring that messy life stuff through the gilded doors of this office."

Even a few hundred years on, America is still deeply rooted in the Protestant Work Ethic's (sometimes called the Puritan Work Ethic) values of stoicism and long-suffering. This is the nation that brought you John Wayne, Clint Eastwood and Curt Schilling's bloody sock. America is the birthplace of Sooners, pioneers and prospectors; wimps need not apply. Perhaps this is why, in a land filled with mental illness, we remain so intolerant of it.

The lifetime prevalence of some sort of diagnosable mental illness is 46%; nearly half of the people reading this book could be formally diagnosed at some point in their life. If you are not, or have never been mentally ill, someone you love certainly has been or will be. Why then, do we read statistics like the following?[XVIII]

70% of the population would not want someone with depression to marry into their family (Barnhardt, 2003).

Only 19% of respondents said they would feel comfortable around someone with mental illness (Harris, 1991).[XIX]

Lamy (1996) found that people with mental illness were viewed more dangerously than ex-convicts.[XX]

Sayce (2003) discovered that 73% of those portrayed on TV as having mental illness are dangerous (e.g., deranged killer).[XXI]

The facts are astounding – many of us are crazy but we don't like crazy people. Inevitably, some percentage of the 70% of people that disliked the idea of a depressed person marrying into their family were depressed themselves. After all, 25% of our nation is on psychotropic medications at any given time. We have all been touched by mental illness, but for various reasons, we are terrified of it.

But perhaps terror is not the right word, maybe a more appropriate term is "morbid fascination." After all, psychology is still the second most commonly pursued college degree (English is the first), a reality that many feel stems from matriculants desire to "figure themselves out." A recent Forbes article entitled, "Why Crazy People Make Better Bloggers"[XXII] enumerated some of the reasons why the writing of the troubled is so widely read. Maybe we the disdain we feel for "craziness" is simply discomfort with the unknown; a discomfort many of us actively try to manage through indirect engagement.

Far from being the unequivocal bad it has been portrayed to be, mental illness is a complicated matter that needs a second look. Anyone who has suffered with mental illness (the author slowly raises his hand) can attest, it is nothing to be desired or glorified. However, I believe a more nuanced look at its impact on empathy, creativity and other desirable outcomes can help lessen some of its attendant stigma.

A CAUTIONARY CAVEAT

Before I dive into all the reasons why I feel you should "fly the crazy flag" let me say a word about the manner in which I'll discuss mental illness here. As a psychologist, I am not naïve to the damaging impact of serious mental illness. I mean no disrespect when I speak of mental disorders as "weirdness" or "craziness." Quite the opposite, I hope to alleviate some of the pain in the world by making mental illness less scary and sterile.

It has been my observation that part of the reason why people remain silent about their internal struggles is that they don't want to be labeled, treated differently and kid-gloved. There is nothing normal about being normal and the sooner we can own that and start laughing about it, the sooner people with serious problems will be able to come forward. We give power to mental illness when we reverence it. Perhaps a little greater informality would lead to a great deal more acceptance.

WHY YOU SHOULD FLY
THE CRAZY FLAG

We are a nation founded on "life, liberty and the pursuit of happiness." The belief that all men are free and that that freedom should be used to pursue happiness is part of our national DNA. Unfortunately, I think we fail to look deeply into the Founders' words. We are guaranteed life and liberty, they were our God-given due in the minds of the authors of the Constitution. Happiness however, was to be pursued, but not was not promised to anyone necessarily. We forget this, feeling happiness should be our right, our "default mode." Perhaps this is part of why the mentally ill become pariahs in our society – they defy our unrealistic dream that everyone should be happy all of the time. By ostracizing them, we are free to keep living out the fantasy that happiness is the only emotion worth having.

While we may prize happiness above all other emotions, a growing body of research is showing that, in order to be truly great, we would be well served to embrace the entire gamut of the emotional spectrum. Take Attention Deficit Hyperactivity Disorder (ADHD), a disorder that impacts roughly 5% of American youth.[XXIII] Distractibility and a lack of impulse control are just two of the basic features of this disorder and both sound problematic, right? Well, kind of.

Researchers on creative thinking gave 60 students, 30 of whom were diagnosed with ADHD and 30 of whom were not, a series of tests and recorded the results.[XXIV] The tests measured creativity across a number of contexts including drama, music, humor, creative writing and scientific discovery, measuring 10 domains in total. In each of the 10 domains, those with ADHD were shown to be more creative and skilled at brainstorming than their "normal" peers. Another "troubled" group that has shown heightened levels of creativity are those diagnosed with mania. Mania is a state of abnormally elevated mood that could almost be thought of as the opposite of depression. Just as with ADHD, hypomanic (that is, slightly manic) individuals tend to be more creative and more prolific than their non-diagnosable peers.[XXV]

What of depression, the mood state most antithetical to the ideal of American happiness? One of the hallmark features of depression is "rumination" – a tendency to replay and roll scenarios around in one's mind again and again. While this can be debilitating when the recycled messages are self-injurious, it can also lead to sound decision-making. In what is being referred to as the "analytical rumination hypothesis" depressed people are better able to zero in on a problem, reducing external distractions and other "mind noise" and examine the problem more deeply than their more optimistic counterparts. The tendency toward rumination, when pointed in the right direction can have a focusing effect that allows for thoughtful decision-making. One striking example of this is a recent study that shows that among people with late stage illnesses, those with the highest sense of personal well being were more likely to die in the short term future than the "mildly content." It would seem that a sense of heightened well being can lead you to believe that all is well, and overlook serious threats.[XXVI]

In the lifelong struggle for "half-full vs. half-empty", depressed folks (we prefer to be called "realists") have recently won some major bragging rights as research is beginning to point to something called "depressive realism." Depressive realism is the notion that the slightly morose see the world more accurately than do their Polyanna-ish counterparts. Happy people suffer from a variety of rose-colored delusions about the world including locus of control and optimism bias. Locus of control bias means that they feel they are more in control or powerful than is actually the case and optimism bias is the tendency to overestimate the occurrence of positive life events (and underestimate the probability of negative life events).

Moderately depressed individuals tend to give more accurate ratings of their own power as well as the likelihood of certain positive and negative events occurring in their life. It would seem that the cognitive defense mechanisms that shield happy people from the tough realities of life may also make them slightly out of touch and less well prepared to make tough decisions. What's more, the anhedonia, or lack of enjoyment of pleasurable activities, that accompanies depression ensures that we remain intently focused on the task at hand – learning from and solving the problem that is troubling us. For years, evolutionary psychologists have agonized over why something as widespread as depression seems to be hanging around. After all, over millennia, the body tends to rid itself of non-adaptive elements and the brain tends to de-bug errors in it's programming. It now seems increasingly probable that depression is here to stay and with very good reason.[XXVII]

LEADERSHIP AND MENTAL ILLNESS

The idea that mental travails bring about greatness is not new, but recent research has done much to clarify and expand our thinking in that area. Aristotle stated as early as the fourth century B.C. "that all men who have attained excellence in philosophy, in poetry, in art and in politics, even Socrates and Plato, had a melancholic habitus; indeed some suffered even from melancholic disease." We are even more familiar with the popular notion that suffering is prerequisite to producing great art. Keats agrees saying, "Do you not see how necessary a World of Pains and troubles is to school an intelligence and make it a soul?" As is so often the case, science is only now bearing out what the truly observant have been saying for centuries – mental anguish can sometimes breed greatness.

One believer in the notion that a troubled life can breed a great leader is Dr. Nassir Ghaemi, author of "A First Rate Madness." Ghaemi begins his book with the general point that he spends the rest of the piece driving home, "…in at least one vitally important circumstance, insanity produces good results and sanity is a problem." Ghaemi says that four key elements of certain mental illnesses – mania and depression – seem to promote leadership excellence in times of crisis. In particular, he finds that manic and mildly depressed leaders are more realistic, resilient, empathic and creative. We have discussed mental illness, realism and creativity above, but what about mental illness promotes resilience and empathy?

We have all had the experience of suffering a loss or a period of difficulty that made us more acutely aware of the pain involved. In 2011 and 2012 my wife and a I lost two babies, something that had also happened to a number of our friends. Prior to our own loss, I was certainly sympathetic and saddened by the news of my friends' miscarriages, but I was not profoundly impacted by it, nor could I honestly say that I felt a great deal of personal empathy for their loss. Since our own loss, Katrina and I have a deepened understanding of the pain that attends the loss of a child. As a result, we are much better positioned to comfort and succor our loved ones in the sad case of a similar event. Such is also the case with leaders in times of crisis.

Leaders who have had to struggle to overcome personal demons, are often loved by their people as they go through times of crisis as a group. Both Martin Luther King Jr. and Gandhi attempted suicide as youths and both suffered bouts of major depression in their adult lives as well. Having been through that dark valley on their own and having lived to tell the story, they were both living proof of the power of resilience. What's more, their ability to identify with a struggling people imbued their messages with an empathetic power that moved mountains.

PROTECTIVE PAIN

Gabby Gingras was, in many respects, a parent's dream. She never cried when the doctor pricked her for a blood test and was unphased by the bumps and bruises that send other toddlers into hysterics. But while this imperviousness to pain sounds great to tired parents everywhere, it actually has a much more devastating impact. Gabby cannot feel pain – and this reality places her in great danger. Gabby was born with what is known as "congenital insensitivity to pain" also known as "congenital analgesia." Those who suffer from congenital analgesia cannot feel and have never felt pain, and thus, have difficulty distancing themselves from problem behaviors that may cause harm. As Gabby's mother says, "Pain teaches. Pain protects. Pain can save you from a lot of bad things in life."

Gabby and others like her are prone to a number of harmful behaviors that make each new developmental milestone a new source of worry for her parents. Budding teeth mean that she may now bite her tongue or chew through her lip. "She started cutting teeth and she had bit down through the skin. She would have bit down to the bone had I let her.", Gabby's mother Trish recalls. Her father adds, "We decided to pull her teeth because she was mutilating her fingers."[XXVIII]

First steps, anxiously awaited by most parents, simply mean a new set of hazards for parents of a child with congenital analgesia. By her second birthday, Gabby had been hospitalized numerous times from spills that had not registered as dangerous or painful. Of even greater concern was her tendency to stick her fingers in her eyes, a common occurrence for children with pain insensitivity. Mr. Gingras recalls, "You'd look away for one second, you'd look back and she'd have her fingers in her eye. You're watching your child go blind right in front of you." Gabby eventually had to have her left eye removed entirely and her right eye remains very damaged.

These days Gabby is doing much better — she's a 10-year old enrolled fifth grader enrolled at Liberty Elementary in Big Lake, Minnesota. Her left eye has been replaced with a non-functional prosthesis, and although she is legally blind, she only has to wear protective goggles when she sleeps. Gabby is spunky with an indefatigable spirit which has made her a media darling. She has now appeared on a Who's Who of talk shows including stop on "Maury", "Montel" and "Oprah" in addition to appearances on every major news network. Older and wiser now, Gabby is able to understand what she can and cannot do, but cannot fall back on her senses the way that most of us do. She is in every respect a "normal" girl; an avid Taylor Swift fan and an excellent student. But Gabby's story is a lesson to us all about the protective power of pain. Pain teaches us and sets the bounds within which we live our life. Pain instructs and places helpful parameters around our every day. And while Gabby's insensitivity to pain is a physical problem, it is easy to hypothesize that being impervious to emotional pain could have similarly devastating consequences.

SUFFERING IS AS GOOD
AS YOU MAKE IT

Aristotle's words echo those of Gabby's mother, "Learning is not child's play; we cannot learn without pain." I began this chapter with a caveat about suffering; I have not and do not wish to glorify suffering for its own sake. After all, Aristotle also said (and I agree) that, "Happiness is the meaning and the purpose of life, the whole aim and end of human existence." This is not an exercise in mid-century morality in the "it builds character" sense either. Suffering is amoral; it is what we do with the things that happen to us that determines whether or not we will be broken or exalted by the breaks we've gotten.

Viktor Frankl is the Austrian psychiatrist whose recounting of his experiences in the concentration camps of World War II has inspired so many. Dr. Frankl was understandably spiritually broken by what he observed in the camps. He despaired for his own life, the life of his family and for the soul of humanity as he witnessed the horrors of camp life. However, Dr. Frankl made an amazing discovery that would go on to inform his new school of psychotherapy, later called "logotherapy." Dr. Frankl found that Nietzsche had been on to something when he had observed that "He has a why to live can bear with almost any how." Prisoners that were able to couch their suffering in terms of something meaningful lived longer and were more resilient than those who become mired in the day-to-day atrocities perpetrated against them.

Seeing this trend, Dr. Frankl began to search for his own raison d'etre, eventually settling on cataloguing and understanding the psychological implications of what he was observing and recording it for the benefit of humankind. His work, "Man's Search for Meaning" has gone on to become one of the best selling books of all time, providing inspiration to millions around the world. As Viktor Frankl said so beautifully, "Between stimulus and response there is a space. In that space is our power to choose our response. In our response lies our growth and freedom."

Despite our fondest desires, we cannot choose much of what happens to us. People we love will break our heart, leave and disappoint us; all without our permission! Ideas we love will fail and we will make mistakes. For better or worse, imperfection is a part of this journey we're on, it's a given. What is less certain and infinitely more important is how we will react to this imperfection. Will we let pain teach us or break us? Will disappointment set protective parameters for future ventures or discourage us from ever trying again? Will heartbreak deepen our empathy for others' suffering or make us callous? So, maybe you've been through some tough stuff. Perhaps life has treated you unfairly. And maybe, just maybe, you're a little bit crazy from all the things that you've been through. That was all out of your hands, but was is squarely in your control is whether or not you'll be the generous, humane, productive kind of crazy or just someone's weird aunt.

THE WAY FORWARD

In what can only be called the result of misguided projection, we have demonized difference in others because we are afraid of it in ourselves. In a culture where happiness is the greatest currency, we have ostracized those who have difficulty grinning and bearing it. In so doing, we have missed opportunities to be instructed by our own sadness and overlooked the genius that so often cohabitates with "madness." The way forward will require us to first embrace the "crazy" in ourselves, learning that deviations from happiness can be just as valuable as that most sought after (and transient) of emotional states. Once we have come to terms with our own emotional variability, we will better positioned to react with understanding toward our fellow man. The way forward will be difficult, but starts with the following:

Fly Your Crazy Flag – There is a great deal of pressure, especially in professional circles, to show others that you "have your stuff together." Although we may be bubbling on the inside, we are taught not to speak about whatever may be going on, in the service of others being able to interact with us in sterile and predictable ways. Odds are, you've internalized this widely held social more just by virtue of its ubiquity. Consider your reaction if, upon having an asked an acquaintance, "How are you doing?" they countered with an actual account of their current struggles rather than they typical, "Fine, you?" Would you be surprised? Would you be upset at them for placing the burden of empathy on you? Now, what if I asked you respond with complete honesty the next ten times you were greeted with that same phrase? How would you react? By and large, our culture promotes a sort of pseudo-intimacy that gives the appearance of emotional connection but lacks any real teeth. It is possible to be asked, "How are you?" ten or more times in a day and not have a single person really want to know the answer.

But before you go shaking your finger at the unfairness of an emotionally disconnected society, I'd like for you to consider your own role in this mess we've all co-created. If you are withholding imperfections about yourself that would normalize others' pain, you are implicated. If you vocally criticize others for the "weirdnesses" you dislike most about your own behavior, you are implicated. Imagine the collective sigh of relief we could all breathe if all of us were just honest about the things we didn't like about ourselves and the things that scared us. Not in a moaping, "woe is me" kind of way, but rather in the "it is what it is and I'm working on it" kind of way. One thing I learned early in my life as a therapist and executive coach is that outward appearances can be very deceiving. We are acutely aware of our own quirks but seem blind to the fact that the rich, privileged and beautiful wrestle with many of the same demons we do.

Commit today to being a part of the solution. I know there are things you've experienced that could comfort someone else. I know there are weaknesses that you hold back for fear of others not accepting you. The irony of that is, that until you lay all your cards on the table, you will always view their acceptance of you as conditional. "He only likes me because he can't see the REAL me", you tell yourself. "If she knew what I was really like, she'd run." With your crazy flag at half-mast, you'll never know true, unconditional love and acceptance, because you've withheld that opportunity from others. Only by flying it high will you be able to separate those who truly support you from those who support only the "perfect" shell of you.

Lead Like Crazy – As you read above, what we've historically thought of us psychological pitfalls can actually have substantial upside in the way you lead others. The first step, however, is to realize that you are a leader. The most succinct definition of leadership I know is, "influencing people to work in service of a common goal." Too often we conflate the idea of leadership with having a corporate position of prominence or wielding political or financial power. The first step toward leading like crazy is to know that you are a leader. If you have ever coordinated a book drive for your kid's PTA – you are a leader. If you have ever made calls on behalf of a local charity – you are a leader. If you have ever herded a family of stragglers out the door – you are a leader.

Once you've embraced your inner leader (corny, I know), it's time to realize what made Dr. King, Gandhi, Lincoln and others so great. Typically, we think of leaders as being larger than life – superhuman even, but that is simply not the case. Lincoln was a failed businessman who had lost multiple political contests. All of the leaders mentioned above suffered with sometimes debilitating self-doubt. And all of that so-called weakness was their greatest strength. Why's that you ask? Because it turns out that we don't want superhuman leaders, we want leaders that are relatable, slightly better versions of ourselves.

Leaders aren't typically found at the head of the class. Indeed, leaders are typically slightly taller, slightly heavier, and only slightly smarter than the people they lead. People want to see themselves in the people that are leading them. They want to imagine having a beer with that person, or spending an evening laughing with them, not be lead by some big-brained automaton. So, if you're a little crazy, not in great shape and are plagued my misgivings about your own worth – you're in really excellent company. Remember, you are a leader. Whether or not you become a great leader has less to do with how innately awesome you are and much more to do with how you leverage your pain to show others that you're a lot like them. The scars are there, whether or not you're courageous enough to share them with your followers is what will make all the difference.

Find Purpose in Pain – You've probably heard all your life that "everything happens for a reason." This is utter bullshit. Now, whoever told you this probably meant well. Perhaps you were having a tough time and they, seeking to comfort you, wanted to assuage that pain by making it seem fateful. The fact is though, bad stuff just happens, sometimes for no reason at all. And while that may be the case, it doesn't mean there is nothing you can learn from the suffering that comes in to your life.

Hardship disrupts complacency. Hardship is binary. Suffering strips us of our ability to be neutral, to not decide, to be the Switzerland of personal growth and development. When tough stuff happens to us, we are brought to a crossroads with one road leading to learning and growth and the other leading to helplessness and cynicism. Whether or not what happened to you was supposed to be is immaterial. Maybe it was part of a plan that God, the Universe or whoever is up there had for you. Maybe it was a random bit of bad luck. Whatever the case, it happened, and dealing with it is going to get you feeling better a lot faster than trying to ascertain the meaning of it all.

There is no shame or redemption in having undergone difficulty, it's as universal as the common cold and nothing about hardship makes you deep per se. What separates those who lead great lives from those who do not is the way in which they handle the inevitability of bad things happening to good people. And while the hardship itself may not carry with it any implicit meaning, the way you handle it most certainly can. It is my sincere wish that your life is kept as free of hardship as humanly possible, I'm no glutton for punishment. But as much as I may wish it otherwise, you and I have both have tough battles yet to fight. When those battles do arrive, I'm hopeful that you will choose the path of growth, learning and increased empathy rather than the road to nihilism and disillusionment.

LIVED LEARNING EXERCISES

*Consider for a moment the hardest thing that has ever happened to you. Now, consider five ways in which you are a better, kinder, more empathic person as a result of having been through this particular hardship. If you find that you have chosen the path of bitterness as a result of this suffering, determine five ways in which you might re-channel this experience for your own growth and learning.

* Keeping in mind the difficulty discussed above, identify a person or a group of people you might comfort or assist as a result of what you've been through. LGBT adults who struggled before might assure questioning youth that "it gets better." Victims of bullying might reach out to bullies and the bullied alike to deepen their understanding of the pains of being picked on. Those who have last a loved one are well positioned to "mourn with those who mourn and comfort those who stand in need of comfort." Whatever your personal struggle, be assured that it can be made more meaningful as you apply your learning in the service of your fellowman.

CHAPTER FOUR

A LOT OF WHAT YOU BELIEVE IS WRONG

Having invested a few hours of your time in reading this book so far, I feel as though I'm getting to know you a little better. In fact, I feel like I know you well enough to make some suppositions about your personality preferences. Let me give it a shot; consider the following statements in terms of how true they are of you and let me know how I did.

"Although others may see you as put together, inside you are worrisome and insecure. You want to be admired by others and you think about this when making decisions. Although you may not have done big things yet, you feel like that day will come. You feel as though you have a lot of untapped potential. You're an independent thinker who thoughtfully considers ideas before accepting them. You enjoy a certain amount of variety and change and dislike being restrained by restrictions or limitations. You know you're not perfect, but you are typically able to use your personality strengths to compensate for your weaknesses."

So, how did I do? On a scale from 1 to 5, with 5 being the most accurate, how accurately would you say I described your personality? If you're like most people, you probably ranked that description of you as a 4 or 5, which likely puzzled you since we've never met. The paragraph above illustrates what is called "Barnum Effect" or alternately, "Fortune Cookie Effect". Barnum Effect is named for P.T. Barnum, the great entertainer and circus magnate.

Barnum famously posited that "There's a sucker born every minute" and used his knowledge of how to sucker people to get them to part with their money. Barnum's understanding of suckers, though born under the big top, undoubtedly surpasses that of many formally trained academicians. P.T. understood what psychologists call "confirmation bias" or the human tendency to look for information that reinforces ideas we already hold.

When we receive feedback about ourselves there are two simultaneous dynamics that make up the broader phenomenon of confirmation bias. The first of these is "self-verification" which is the tendency to reinforce existing beliefs. The second is "self-enhancement" whereby we attend to information that makes us feel good about ourselves. The function of these two dynamics is clear – to maintain our self esteem and feelings of confidence. In general this is a positive, after all, who doesn't want to feel about themselves? However, these dynamics work in overdrive in a number of instances – including when our deeply held-beliefs are challenged or our self-esteem is challenged. Confirmation bias becomes problematic when it leads us to maintain the status quo in the face of disconfirmatory information or overlook realistic, negative feedback about ourselves. In these instances, our need to feel competent can cause us to ignore warnings and worse yet, to hate.[XXXI]

THE PERSISTENCE OF BELIEF

As is so often the case, the humanities have long observed what science is only now beginning to explain in greater detail – personal beliefs are hard to extinguish, even in the face of evidence that they are untrue. Fifth Century Greek Historian Thucydides wrote, "it is a habit of mankind…to use sovereign reason to thrust aside what they do not fancy."[XXXII] Sir Francis Bacon posited that, "The human understanding when it has once adopted an opinion…draws all things else to support and agree with it. And though there be a greater number and weight of instances to be found on the other side, yet these it either neglects or despises, or else by some distraction sets aside or rejects."

But perhaps no one has written on the topic as lucidly as Leo Tolstoy who wrote, "I know that most men – not only those considered clever, but even those who are very clever, and capable of understanding most difficult scientific, mathematical or philosophical problems – can very seldom discern even the simplest and most obvious truth if it be such as to oblige them to admit the falsity of conclusions they have formed, perhaps with much difficulty – conclusions of which they are proud, which they have taught to others, and on which they have built their lives."[XXXIII] Simply put, once we have formed an opinion, especially one central to our worldview, we cling tenaciously to that opinion even when the facts may speak to its wrongheadedness.

THE SCIENCE OF BELIEF

The 2004 Presidential campaign pitted the incumbent President George W. Bush against the Democratic challenger John Kerry. It also provided an opportunity for brain researchers to study the science of what makes belief so "sticky." Researchers began by gathering candidates who professed have a well-defined presence for one candidate over the other. Participants were given seemingly contradictory statements either from President Bush, Senator Kerry, or a third politically neutral public figure.

They were also given further information that made the seeming contradiction appear more plausible. They were then asked to determine whether or not the individuals in questions had in fact made statements that were inconsistent.

During the evaluation and thought process, research participants were monitored inside a magnetic resonance imaging (MRI) machine that allowed the scientists to observe their brain activity. As subjects evaluated seemingly contradictory statements made by their less-preferred candidate, the emotional centers of their brain remained inactive. This allowed them to make cold, rational judgments about these statements. However, as the subjects evaluated the statements of their preferred candidate, the emotional centers of their brain became highly aroused. When the results were tallied, there were clear differences in the evaluations.

Subjects were very likely to endorse their less preferred candidate as having said something contradictory and were highly unlikely to say the candidate of their choice had made such a rhetorical error. Simply put, when their guy said something incorrect, their emotions drown it out, but when "the other guy" said something implausible, they rationally pointed out the fallacious thinking. [XXXIV] The inference we can draw from this experiment is that the emotional tumult created when facts collided with logic fell down on the side of emotion. Belief is an emotional construct, we feel it deeply, and are loathe to let silly facts tell us that we believe is not so. This emotional reaction created a situation whereby the status quo was maintained and previously held beliefs were confirmed, even when logic would have suggested otherwise. In simple terms, we rationally evaluate things that do not intersect with our worldview and emotionally evaluate those that do.

THE PERILS OF FREE CHOICE

Let's pretend for a moment that you have agreed to be a part of a study I'm conducting. I bring you in to a room and present you with six works of art, shown below. I then ask to you to rank order the six paintings from 1 to 6, with 1 being your most preferred and 6 being your least preferred. I further explain that you'll be able to leave today with a painting of your choosing. Please take a few minutes and rank the pictures below from 1 to 6 based on your personal preferences.

(PICTURES OF SIX PAINTINGS)

Now that you've completed the ranking assignment, I tell you that you can choose any one of the six paintings. Naturally you choose Number 1 seeing as how it was your most preferred and I retire to the back of the room to retrieve it. I return shortly with a worried look and apologetically tell you that the paintings you ranked 1, 2, 5 and 6 are all picked over, leaving the ones you ranked 3 and 4 remaining. You can still have your pick of either 3 or 4 and you decide on 3 given that it was your slight preference.

Now imagine that I give you two weeks off and invite you back into my office to rank the same six paintings in order of your preference. What do you hypothesize will have happened? Would your preferences remain the same or would they have shifted? What might account for them changing or staying the same?

Well, if you are like most people who participate in this experiment (commonly referred to as the "Free Choice Paradigm") your preferences will have changed upon your return. Typically we see the painting that was chosen, previously ranked Number 3 will now have progressed into the Number 2 spot. Conversely, the painting that was not chosen, previously ranked Number 4, will now have fallen into the Number 5 spot. What accounts for such a dramatic change over such a short period of time? After all, both of the paintings represented a sort of middling preference, neither greatly prized or greatly disliked at the initial ranking. So how they have now migrated closer to the respective poles? Once again, the answer lies in our need to be special and to think of ourselves as competent, capable decisions makers who make choices based on rational criteria.

Dr. Dan Gilbert, Harvard professor and happiness researcher extraordinaire describes the thought process of participants thusly, "The one I got is really better than I thought. That other one I didn't get sucks."[XXXV] Once the participant has adopted an opinion, they begin to construct a list of reasons why their choice was the right one. Perhaps they tell themselves that they prefer the shading or the texture, or the way the painting frames a previously blank space in the living room. Whatever the specific reasons we are prone to build up our decisions immediately upon having made a commitment. What's more, we play the other side of the fence too and begin to mount an offensive against the road not taken. We are at least as tenacious at tearing down the unchosen option as we are at building up our commitment, just ask anyone who has ever been broken up with by a partner that they "didn't like anyway."

The phenomenon mentioned above, whereby we talk up choices we've made and denigrate those we've passed on probably makes intuitive sense, but what if it goes deeper than that. Dan Gilbert and his team examined the impact of the Free Choice Paradigm on a group of subjects with anterograde amnesia; in other words, a group of hospitalized individuals unable to form new memories. Like their neurotypical (that is, without brain damage) peers, the amnesiac patients were asked to rank the paintings from 1 to 6 and were given the option to keep either painting 3 or 4. Upon choosing a painting, the researchers promised to mail the chosen painting in a few days and left the room.

Returning just 30 minutes later, the members of Dr. Gilbert's team reintroduced themselves to the amnesiacs who, unable to form new memories, had no recollection of having met with them before or having performed the exercise. To ensure that the amnesic patients were truly unable to form memories, the researchers then asked them to point to the painting that they had chosen before, a task at which the patients performed less well than chance guessing! The patients are then put through the whole ranking exercise again, with astonishing results. Just as with the neurotypical control group, the amnesic patients "talked up" the choice they made and dismissed the painting not chosen, even though they had no memory of having made a choice at all! Clearly, our need to view ourselves as competent and intelligent lives somewhere so deeply within us that not even cognitive impairment can touch it.

POLARIZATION

As we've seen above, the very act of making a decision can move us away from moderation. Pair this tendency with the confirmation bias tendency to surround ourselves with like-minded others and you have a recipe for conflict, polarization and even extremism. Dick Cheney famously personified this tendency when he demanded that only Fox News be playing when he entered the room. The Vice President, highly criticized by his Democratic counterparts and liberal news outlets like MSNBC, wanted to surround himself with less critical viewpoints. And while it's easy to pick on Vice President Cheney (he shot someone in the face for crying out loud!) we are all guilty of surrounding ourselves with like-minded others.

In general, we flock to those with whom we share a cultural, religious, political or ideological identity. In so doing, we surround ourselves with a chorus of "Yes People" who reinforce the validity of our opinions.[XXXVI] Given the emotional wrangling we see is involved with confronting conflicting ideas, immersing ourselves in an ideologically homogenous pool is infinitely easier than the alternative. If everyone with whom we associate looks, acts and thinks like we do, we are able to "successfully" skirt a number of tough internal struggles.

THE GROUP IS DUMBER THAN THE SUM OF ITS PARTS

Some within-group socializing is natural and even healthy. Church groups offer social and financial support to their congregants. Groups of LGBTQ youth gather to express their shared joys and struggles and learn that, "It gets better." In these and myriad other instances, groups of like minded people find support and encouragement that propels them toward bigger and better things. When intragroup homogeneity becomes problematic however, is when the need to maintain group purity leads to a lack of "cross-pollenization" between groups of different minds. Homogenous groups lead to what is called "group polarization", a potentially dangerous dynamic.

Until the early 1960's the prevailing theory of group risk-taking behavior was what is called "normalization theory", the idea that group decisions would reflect an average of the norms of the people that comprised it. However, a 1961 Master's thesis paper by J.A. Stoner[XXXVII] began to question the normalization theory and propose what we now call group polarization – the tendency of a group to engage in behaviors and hold opinions more extreme than the average group member. The reasons why group polarization occur are complex, but some suggest that diffusion of responsibility is to blame. Members of the group feel more comfortable putting forth an extreme position because direct responsibility is less likely to accrue to them. Further, given that group members cannot read each others' minds, they may also assume a degree of comfort or agreement with a polarizing viewpoint since they assume that the corpus of the group is also in agreement. Given these and other group dynamics, members become emboldened and take increasingly strident positions, comforted by the size of the group and the potential for anonymity if things go poorly. [XXXVIII]

So, what does this have to do with much of what you believe being wrong? As we discussed at the beginning of this chapter, the confirmation bias means that you seek out and internalize information that is a. consistent with what you already believe and b. is what you want to hear. Right from the outset, your lens is skewed toward maintaining the status quo and selective attention, not truth and growth. Next, we learned that as new information enters your view that might challenge your current opinions, you ward off those attacks by emotionally overriding inconvenient logic. As you make new choices and reinforce existing beliefs, you build up the beliefs you hold and tend to tear down those you don't to make your worldview seem that much more veracious. And finally, you surround yourself with a group of like-minded individuals who nod approvingly at everything you espouse. All the while this group with which you affiliate is helping to de-centralize your opinion and move you further from the "others." Is it any wonder then that there is some convenient untruth in the things you claim to know? The brain is a primitive creature – set up to maintain ego at the expense of enlightenment. For those concerned about living a meaningful life rather than just an easy life, it takes some commitment and some unlearning to move forward.

THE FANTASY CYCLE

To describe confirmation bias in a nutshell, is to say that it is "seeing the world as we wish it were, not as it truly is." Described thusly, confirmation bias doesn't sound all that bad. After all, in a world of wars and famines, can't we a let a little Pollyanna-ish blindness slide? Truly conceptualized, most of our big concerns in life are highly nuanced and have infinite shades of grey. God, love, and relationships between diverse groups, to name just a few, are seldom as cut and dried as we might like. Engaging in wishful, rather than truthful, thinking leads us to engage in something called the "Fantasy Cycle" that looks something like this:[XXXIX]

Dream Stage – Through selective attention, emphasizing convenient truths and surrounding ourselves with like minded others, we create a world that supports our preferred belief system. We are comfortable in this world and are seldom asked to question our "pet truths."

Frustration Stage – We are confronted with realities that are inconsistent with the world as we wish to see it. Often times, this leads us to cling ever more firmly to our desired beliefs and shield ourselves from inconvenient truths.

Nightmare Stage – Our fantasy has now become a nightmare as the things we once believed are shown to be increasingly incompatible with reality. We are no longer able to cling to our previous notions of the truth and experience what is referred to as an "explosion into reality" where we are abruptly brought face to face things we wish were not so but are.

The prospect of being thrust into the Nightmare Stage is daunting; the name alone is ominous. To protect ourselves from something of this nature, we may take a number of tacks, none of which lead to a more robust or fulfilled life. We may stop learning to keep new, conflicting information for entering our view. We may become increasingly intractable in our current, self-serving views. Finally, we may withdraw from any groups that challenge our thought processes and deepen our associations with our particular "in crowd."

We have seen above that our cognitive processes are set up to be parsimonious, not enlightened. Our brains, left to their own devices, make life easy, not good. And while this doesn't make life fulfilling, it does make some utilitarian sense. After all, we are confronted with myriad decisions daily – what color suit to wear, what to have for breakfast, how to proceed in a relationship – can you really blame us for wanting to put some of our thought processes on auto-pilot?! The trick, I think, is to auto-pilot on things that are of little consequence but to withhold judgment and accept greater ambiguity on things that matter. Odds are, you can drive to the store half asleep. You can buy the same milk, park in the same spot, and choose the same deodorant all without any adverse consequences. However, when we judge people with the same automatic nonchalance with which we buy milk, we have a problem.

THE PATH FORWARD

Hopefully by now you're convinced by now that questioning some of your deeply held assumptions, while difficult, is a worthwhile undertaking. Rene Descartes, considered by many to be the father of Modern Philosophy did something similar when he sought out to question everything he thought he know, famously arriving at the one thing he could know for certain, "Cogito ergo sum (I think therefore I am)."

Granted, Descartes exercise is a little impractical, but it does set a positive precedent in some respects. So much of what we assume we "know" has been passed down to us somewhat uncritically. We've accepted the lessons we've learned from our parents, teachers and the other salient personal and cultural influences that have been instrumental in shaping our worldview. Would it really be so bad to give some of that a second look – leaving what we no longer found to be true and newly embracing timeless truths?

The truth is, Americans tend to applaud certainty in much the same way and for many of the same reasons we so admire innate giftedness. This is a land that cheers on confident politicians and castigates "flip-floppers." Numerous studies have shown that many of the "talking heads" we revere, notably those in financial services, are no more adept at predicting stock moves than random chance. Despite their inability to outperform a dartboard, we continue to look to them and pay them exorbitant salaries. Why? Because they are incorrect with boldness. Surety is baseball, red meat and the pioneer spirit. Doubt seems wimpy and Continental. In order to recreate a more veracious personal worldview, we must first stop looking at doubt as a sign of weakness and view it as the emotional and intellectual sign of maturity it most truly is.

When attempting to override our cognitive autopilot, there are at least three easy ways to get started. They are:

Be a Truth Scientist – We hold information that we want to believe and information that we do not want to believe to different standards. When a piece of information is presented to us that is consistent with our desired beliefs, we tend to ask, "Why CAN I believe this?" We look for confirmatory evidence, and in so doing, are likely to find bits and pieces of it, at which time we prematurely shut down our search for the truth. When a more difficult truth is presented to us, we tend to ask "Why CAN'T I believe this?" and immediately seek out disconfirmatory evidence. In a phrase, we look to support things we like and look to destroy things we don't.

One of the hallmarks of science is that it searches for both confirmatory and disconfirmatory information in the search for truth. Sadly, humans tend to be much more one-sided in their own decision making, with the particular side depending on how hard to hear the answer may be. A person in love is likely to ask, "What are some of the reasons why I should marry this person" but would seldom consider "What might be some of the complications that would arise from marrying this person." A person recovering from a period of long-term unemployment is likely to ask, "What are the benefits of taking this job?" but is unlikely to consider the ways in which taking the role might impede future professional growth. Socrates famously said that, "The unexamined life is not worth living" and it's worth noting that a thorough examination involves a hard look at both sides of the coin.

Be Empathic – Empathy is a term that is oft-used and little understood. As opposed to sympathy which is hierarchical in nature (e.g., I pity you from a place of relative advantage), empathy requires equal footing. If I have empathy for you, it means that to the extent possible, I have put myself in a position to feel what you are feeling and see the world as you do. Groups with opposing viewpoints often express pity for one another but seldom do they operate from a place of true empathy.

The reason empathy is hard to come by has everything to do with our desire not to upset the cognitive simplicity applecart. Dogmatic, firmly held, black and white opinions are nice in that they paint the world in easy to understand ways that adhere to well-defined rules. This idea is good, that idea is bad. This group is doing God's work, this group opposes it. Associate with these people, avoid these others. You are pious, they are evil. Empathy muddies the water by bringing others reasons for acting and think the way they do into sharper relief. We are no longer able to think in absolutist terms, a fact that provides us with infinitely more decisions points along life's way. And while this nuanced approach may represent a more labor intensive process, it also provides a more balanced, thoughtful way of living.

Be a Bridge – Each one of us is a complicated mix of cultures, some of which are seemingly incompatible on their face. Take me for instance. Born in Alabama, I am a Southerner. Raised in the Church of Jesus Christ of Latter-Day Saints I am a Mormon. Trained in the study of human behavior, I am a psychologist. I could also be classified as a husband, father, brother, friend, uncle, boss and mentee, just to name a few cultures to which I belong. The socially conservative values of my geography and religion collide with the left-leaning discipline in which I was schooled. The prevailing religions of my state are antagonistic toward my own faith tradition. The faith tradition in which I practice is antagonistic toward groups of gay and lesbian friends I love and admire. Each of these seeming contradictions has had a real value in my life, however. They have brought me in close proximity to groups of people with vastly different ideas about life and what constitutes truth. That reality has moved me in the direction of greater knowledge and appropriate circumspection about the things I think I know.

Being circumspect about the parameters of our own knowledge makes us thoughtful and slow to judge people with whom we may currently disagree. Bigotry is inherently reductionistic. In order to truly loathe another group, we must distill their essence down into epithets that are catchy, marketable, and induce strong emotions. We must minimize the truth about that group or idea until it becomes a hateful tagline that can fit on a bumper sticker or poster. Intolerance is all about stripping away context; caricatures cannot tolerate nuance.

Empathy on the other hand is about increasing context. A dirty little secret of the psychotherapy community is that therapists don't like all of their clients equally. Some clients are a joy to work with, while others strike anxiety in the hearts of a therapist who sees their initials on the calendar. When I was in practice, I certainly had my favorite clients as well as those whose presenting concerns made me scratch my head. "Why would they do such a thing?", I'd ask myself, puzzling at their self-sabotaging behavior. However, without a single exception, I can say that my respect and empathy for every one of my clients grew as I got to know them better and their lives unfolded before me. Their behavior, while still maladaptive and in need of change, made greater sense to me.

No one gets up in the morning with the aim of being self-defeating, strange, obnoxious and difficult to relate to. We are all "cultural mutts", bundles of self-contradictory ideas and beliefs that we are doing our best to make sense of. Whether or not we position ourselves to gain more light and truth about the world we live in depends largely on whether we take a reductionistic or additive view to the pursuit of knowledge. Will we continue to seek, question and gain ever-deepening understanding about the people and ideas with whom we interact? Or we will take a defensive, reductionistic approach to learning? Seeking to protect what we know from irritating new truths that cause us to question, broaden and perhaps change things we had once believed to be sacrosanct.

If we choose the former, expansive approach, there is simply no substitute for exposure. The limited knowledge that feeds intolerance relies on siloed in-groups lack of interaction. If you are one of "those people", you are easy to hate from a distance as an idea. However, if I sit down with you, discuss your life, and learn more about the reasons you feel as you do, you become humanized to me. Human beings, up close and in all their complexity, are resistant to bigotry. People considered from afar as two-dimensional straw men are easy to hate. It's easy to hate an idea, it's harder to hate a living breathing person. So, whatever your particular cultural encapsulations, know that you can build a bridge to people in other communities and with different ideas. They will be wiser and more empathic for having met you and you them.

LIVED LEARNING EXERCISES

A great deal of misbelief and narrow-mindedness is a byproduct of surrounding ourselves with people who think and act just the same as we do. Consider one group with whom you have currently been in disagreement or have held an opposite point of view. Now, make arrangements to bring yourself in contact with someone from that group and listen to their point of view, without bringing in your own, opposite views on the topic.

Inevitably, you are a part of some group with ideas, beliefs and history worth sharing. Seek out one opportunity to expand the knowledge base of an "outgroup" by sharing with them your own traditions, beliefs and values. Do so non-defensively, and prepare yourself for questions about why you think and act the way you do.

CHAPTER FIVE

YOU'RE NOT AS SAFE AS YOU THINK

Take a moment and imagine the person you love the most. Perhaps it's your spouse or partner; maybe it's a beloved parent. If that person is near, I'd like for you to put the book down and go give them a big hug. Tell them how much you appreciate them and all the reasons why you love them. If they aren't proximal, say a small prayer of thanks or think good thoughts about the positive impact they have in your life before you return to reading. Go on…

…You back now? Ok, great, welcome back.

Now, I want you to realize that the person you've just spent the last few minutes idolizing is more likely to kill you than any stranger, terrorist or bogeyman. In fact, your appendix is more likely to off you than Al Qaida. We have a tendency to fear all of the wrong things. We're scared of high profile, low probability threats like terrorist attacks and home invasions, but we routinely ignore more mundane but probabilistic hazards like not wearing a seatbelt or eating unhealthily. In general, we stink at assessing risk in a number of predictable ways – we don't have all the facts, we're moody, we're control freaks, we think we're unique, we follow the crowd and we are scared of losing. I'd like to touch on each of these in turn and discuss how they impact your ability to live the best kind of life.

YOU DON'T HAVE ALL THE FACTS

Quick! Name all the words you can that begin with the letter "K." Go on, I'm not listening. How many were you able to come up with?

Now, name all of the words you can in which K is the third letter. How many could you name this time?

If you are like most people, you found it easier to generate a list of words that begin with K; the words probably came to you more quickly and were more plentiful in number. But, did you know that there are three times as many words in which K is the third letter than there are that start with K? If that's the case, why is it so much easier to create a list of words that start with K?

It turns out that our mind's retrieval process is far from perfect, and a number of biases play into our ability to recall. Psychologists call this fallibility in your memory retrieval mechanism the "availability heuristic," which simply means that we predict the likelihood of an event based on things we can easily call to mind. Unfortunately for us, the imperfections of the availability heuristic are hard at work as we attempt to gauge the riskiness of different ways of living.

In addition to having a memory better suited to recall things at the beginning and the end of a list, we are also better able to envision things that are scary. I know this first hand. Roughly six years ago, I moved to the North Shore of Hawaii along with my wife for a six-month internship. Although our lodging was humble, we were thrilled to be together in paradise and eager to immerse ourselves in all the local culture and natural beauty it had to offer. That is, until I watched "Shark Week."

For the uninitiated, "Shark Week" is the Discovery Channel's seven-day documentary programming binge featuring all things finned and scary. A typical program begins by detailing sharks' predatory powers, refined over eons of evolution, as they are brought to bear on the lives of some unlucky surfers. As the show nears its end, the narrator typically makes the requisite plea for appreciating these noble beasts, a message that has inevitably been over- ridden by the previous 60 minutes of fear mongering.

For one week straight, I sat transfixed by the accounts of one-legged surfers undeterred by their ill fortune ("Gotta get back on the board, dude") and waders who had narrowly escaped with their lives. Heretofore an excellent swimmer and ocean lover, I resolved at the end of that week that I would not set foot in Hawaiian waters. And indeed I did not. So traumatized was I by the availability of bad news that I found myself unable to muster the courage to snorkel, dive or do any of the other activities I had so looked forward to just a week ago.

In reality, the chance of a shark attacking me was virtually nonexistent. The odds of me getting away with murder (about 1 in 2), being made a Saint (about 1 in 20 million) and having my pajamas catch fire (about 1 in 30 mil- lion), were all exponentially greater than me being bitten by a shark (about 1 in 300 million). My perception of risk was warped wildly by my choice to watch a program that played on human fear for ratings and my actions played out accordingly.

YOU ARE MOODY

One of the reasons psychologists can charge $200 per hour to ask, "how does that make you feel?" is because we have become great at putting fancy-pants labels on things that would otherwise be very intuitive. Take for instance the tongue twisting "affect heuristic," which is simply a reference to our tendency to perceive the world through the lens of whatever mood we are in.

For example, when giving a seminar on risk assessment, I often ask participants to write down the word, that if it were spelled phonetically, would be "dahy." Go on, write it down and don't over think it. It turns out the way you spelled the word has a lot to do with the kind of day you are having. Those that spelled the word as "die" may need a hug, while those that spelled the word "dye" are probably doing fine.

Ask someone having a bad day (those that wrote "die," I'm looking at you) about their childhood and they are likely to tell you how they were chubby, had pimples and never got picked first for kickball. Conversely, ask someone having a good day about their childhood and they are likely to recall summers in Nantucket and triple dips from the Tastee Freeze. Memory and perception are moving targets colored by our mood, not infallible retrieval and evaluation machines through which we make unbiased decisions.

So what is the moral of all of this psychobabble? Think back on the last time you went shopping when you were hungry. Once you've brought that to mind, think back on the contents of your shopping cart. If you're like me, you probably had a whole mess of HoHos, DingDongs, Nutty Buddies and Diet

Coke (you don't want to get fat, after all), but nothing very healthy or substantive.

The same rules apply to any life decision requiring risk assessment; if you try to make decisions when you are happy/sad/angry/in love/anxious/worried/euphoric, you are likely to end up with a life full of junk. So, the next time you are about to make a decision in a fit of rage (or right after getting engaged), take a step back, breathe deeply and let time bring you back down to Earth. After all, shopping while you're hungry can make you sick.

YOU ARE A CONTROL FREAK

We have already touched on people's vested interest in feeling competent and in control. In fact, the definition of stress that I find most useful is "the loss of perceived control over an event." So while the obvious upside of this tendency to feel in control is a perception of personal competence, the downside is that we tend to think we can control random events as well.

Let's say I offered to sell you a lottery ticket with a 1-in-50 chance of winning a prize. How much would you pay if I assigned you a number randomly? Now, how much would you pay if I offered to let you choose your number among the 50 available, allowing you to pick your daughter's birthday?

When psychologists run this experiment, people pay $1.96 on average for the tickets that are given to them and $8.67 on average for the tickets for which they are allowed to choose the number. Obviously, the odds are the same in both conditions (1 in 50), but our confidence that we control the universe is such that we are willing to pay 4.5 times more to be in charge.

Another example of our propensity to overvalue our own influence is the tendency of people to over-invest in their own organization's stock for the stated reason that they can directly impact the stock price. So, Suzie from accounting is going to invest in Coca-Cola because she feels the valuation of the world's greatest brand lives and dies on the skill of her bean counting. Unfortunately, if you—in isolation—can directly impact the rise or fall of your stock, and make personal investment decisions accordingly, you might be going to jail soon. For the rest of us peons, our daily travails do not matter much one way or the other in the ultimate success or failure of a publicly traded company and it is best not to invest as though they do.

YOU THINK YOU ARE UNIQUE

Is your partner out of the room? Good. Now, let your mind wander for a second back to your first high school love. Do you remember how intense your feelings for them were? Do you recall that sick feeling in your gut when you were apart from them? The profound, undeniable sense you had that no one had ever experienced a love as deep or as pure as what you were now feeling for John Q. Quarterback or Jane Q. Cheerleader?

But along the way, something happened and your love went unrequited. You searched for solace from friends, siblings, parents, perhaps even a shrink, all to no avail. Because no matter how many trees you killed in Kleenex form and no matter how many times you told the story of your heartbreak, no one ever got it. How could they after all? Mere mortals could never understand the unique splendor of what you had experienced with your Schnookums. Psychologists call this illusion of uniqueness "personal fable," and it hurts those trying to assess risk at least as much as heartbroken adolescents.

Cook College performed a study in which people were asked to rate the likelihood that a number of positive events (e.g., win the lottery, marry for life) and negative events (e.g., die of cancer, get divorced) would impact their lives. What they found was hardly surprising—participants overestimated the likelihood of positive events by 15% and underestimated the probability of negative events by 20%.[XL]

What this tells us is that we tend to personalize the positive and delegate the dangerous. I might win the lottery, she might die of cancer. We might live happily ever after, they might get divorced. We understand that bad things happen, but in service of living a happy life, we tend to think about those things in the abstract.

The risk management implications of perceived uniqueness are obvious—if we make decisions with the mindset that we are a unique snowflake, we are likely to ignore potential risks. And if we think we are unique, we inevitably ignore lessons from history and from watching others. Worse still, if we perceive upside potential to be "all us" and losing to be the birthright of those other schmucks, we are bound to do stupid things.

YOU FOLLOW THE CROWD

I am privileged to be a part of the speaker's bureau for an investment wholesaler and recently found myself with members of the RS team in San Antonio, Texas. Before my presentation the next day, a few of us decided to grab dinner along San Antonio's historic River Walk. The River Walk is beautiful; tucked one level below the street and lined with restaurants, shops and hotels, it offers no shortage of options for the hungry traveler in search of some authentic Tex-Mex cuisine. After meeting my colleagues at a nearby hotel, we began to wander the labyrinthine streets, passing a number of excellent restaurants but never stopping to eat.

Having not determined any clear criteria for selecting a dinner spot, we continued to wander until we were accosted by an enthusiastic host at a garish Mexican restaurant. After rattling off a list of run-of-the-mill Tex-Mex offerings, he moved on to describing the house drink specials, which sounded similarly unspectacular. So how was it, that just moments later, our five-person party of foodies was seated at a sticky table at this culinary also-ran?

The answer lies in our propensity to try and read others' minds and act in ways that are consistent with their desires—somehow, someway, everyone in our party got the idea that everyone else in the party wanted to eat at this tacky dive and dared not speak up, lest they offend the others. The result was what social scientists call "mismanaged agreement," something illustrated by the classic management tale of "The Abilene Paradox," in which a family drove 100 miles in the scorching Texas heat to eat bad food when all of them really just wanted to stay home.

Our tendency to want to read minds and our inability to do so can result in something much more dire than a stomach full of stale chips, however. This propensity to engage in groupthink is the sort of behavior that leads us to live the life we feel others want us to live instead of the one we truly desire.

As a student of human behavior, there are precious few things that I would state as approximating a law. One of the few ideas that come close for me is that people are cognitively lazy and will consistently use decision-making rules of thumb rather than reinvent the decisional wheel each time. After all, every day of your life is filled with decisions to be made. Diet Coke or Diet Pepsi? Should I exercise or stay in bed? Do I wear the black or the grey suit?

Without heuristics, or experience- based rules of thumb for making deci- sions, life would become paralyzing and we would get very little done. Although there is considerable upside to decision- making heuristics, one of our most common fallbacks is to rely on the deci- sions of others, a trend that can lead us to make poor decisions.

For another example, consider the last time you were asked for money by a person on the street. Perhaps this individual approached you with a cup or a tin, which may or may not have had any money in it already. Stop for a moment and consider who you would more likely donate money to—a person whose cup was empty or someone whose cup showed evidence of the generosity of previous passersby? It seems intuitive that, all other things being equal, the person with the least money in their cup is the one more deserving of your largesse. After all, if they are begging, they may not have adequate financial means to meet their basic human needs. The less money they have, the more they could benefit from your donation, right?

This being the case, why is it that researchers consistently find that passersby give more money to those whose cups already have money? The answer is simple—an empty cup is seen as a judgment of unworthiness by previous onlookers. Although we may not fully comprehend all of the reasons they are unworthy of our donation, we are likely to follow the lead of those who have gone before and with- hold our offering. Switch gears here with me—by basing our decision on the decisions of others, we have over- looked a logical component of deci- sion-making (in this case, need) and relied instead on a choice strategy that may have little to do with what ought to be our primary concern.

These are all the ways in which groupthink can lead us to make unsatisfying decisions (like nasty salsa) and illogical decisions (like helping the wrong person asking for money).

YOU HATE LOSING

The year is 2012. All of those Mayan calendar people you thought were wackos turned out to be right, and the world as we know it is falling apart. Zombies roam the countryside, infecting people with a heretofore unknown disease.

Imagine you are the mayor of a town and you have been approached with two plans. You must make a choice that will have far-reaching implications for the 600 citizens of your once-fair land.

If you adopt Plan A, 200 people will be saved. If you adopt Plan B, there is a 1-in-3 chance that all 600 citizens will be saved but a 2-in-3 chance that none will be saved.

Which decision would you make, mayor? Before you answer, consider two other plans that your vice-mayor just now constructed. If you adopt Plan C, 400 people will die. If you adopt Plan D, there is a 1-in-3 chance that no people will die but a 2-in-3 chance that 600 people will die.

So, which plan did you initially choose: A or B? What about from the second set of alternatives: C or D? If you are like most people, the decisions you made have a great deal to do with your fear of loss. If you take a minute to consider the options, you will notice that options A and C are identical probabilities, as are B and D. That being the case, why is it that people choose A over B at a 3-to-1 ratio, and D over C at a 4-to- 1 ratio? It doesn't make sense, does it? Until you consider the framing of the questions—questions framed as a loss are avoided in both cases. Social psychologists who study loss aversion find that people are typically twice as upset about a loss as they are pleased about a gain.[XLI]

I'm sure it took a decade and millions of dollars to tell you what my dad, a financial advisor, could have told you over lunch. His phone doesn't ring much when he is making people money, but he got a lot of calls in 2008 and 2009. It goes without saying that no one likes to lose (especially money); in this sense our fear of loss is natural and can be protective at times. However, it can also be damaging when it distorts our view of the world or leads us to not even play the game.

Consider the most meaningful thing you have ever done. I would wager it took a measure of risk, uncertainty and hard work to achieve. In this, as with all risk, comes a valuable lesson: to strive for certainty is to doom oneself to mediocrity. Consider the person who remains unattached to avoid risking heartache and finds loneliness in the process. Or the would-be entrepreneur who never makes the leap of faith and wastes a career working at jobs they hate. The irony of obsessive loss aversion is that our worst fears become realized in our attempts to manage them.

THE WAY FORWARD

So, given that we have a number of natural biases in the way we assess threats, how do we approach risk in a way that leads to the best possible life? To some extent or another, we will always be susceptible to the biased lens through which we view the world. However, understanding some of the basic ways in which you misinterpret the dangerousness of the world around you is a good start. Let's consider three ways in which you can refine your lens to better assess the threats and opportunities around you.

Expect to Fail — As with feelings of specialness, perfectionism can actually lead us to disengage from life and not even take appropriate risks. Needing to hit a home run every time you come to bat is a sure way to ride the bench. You know you can't do it, so you sit out. Worse still, you construct a cage of B.S. excuses to protect you from the fact that you're too cowardly to try. When not getting it right the first time and every time is part of the game plan, there is nothing to insulate yourself from. People are weird; this is one of those instance where shooting a little bit lower can help you reach a lot higher.

Do What You Can (and Nothing More) — "Grant me the serenity to accept the things I cannot change, courage to change the things I can, and wisdom to know the difference." Of course, each one of us wants to feel empowered and in control of our lives, but when we lose a realistic grasp on what we control and what we either risk too much or too little. For years, my Mom was afraid to fly. The idea of hurtling through the sky at 30,000 feet in a metal tube terrified her and she missed out on vacations, reunions and seeing the world as a result.

My Mom, along with the rest of world, watched with horror as the events of September 11, 2001 unfolded. But a strange thing happened to her fear of flying in the wake of 9/11; she was no longer afraid. It may seem counterintuitive that such a calamitous event would reduce her fear, but what happened was she became more acutely aware of what she could and could not control. The events of 9/11 were so unforeseen, so horribly unpredictable, that she actually relinquished the idea that she could control some of the more unpredictable things in life and she's been flying ever since.

Feel the Fear and Do It Anyway - Life is funny, absurd even. We spend our lives wringing our hands about grownup monsters in the closet – wild animal attacks, serial killers, killer bees and the like, when in actuality the greatest risks to our health are the things we do every day and never think twice about. Presented with this sort of absurdity, there are really only two options – disengage or feel the fear and do it anyway. Life doesn't provide guarantees and acting as though it does is mad. In an effort to coax certainty out of something that is inherently uncertain, people sometimes disengage or try to make efforts to prepare for every eventuality. Some people hypothesize that hoarding behavior is simply a reaction against this sort of uncertainty and death anxiety (e.g., "You never know when I might need that newspaper article to keep something bad from happening.") These hoarders, who accumulate ostensibly to prepare for the worst actually bring the worst upon themselves. Their belongings fester and the uncleanliness brings about the end it sought to prevent.

Being excessively risk averse brings about a similar dynamic. We disengage from scary things, ostensibly in the pursuit of living a long, happy life. We put off children to prepare to give them the perfect life, and miss our best childbearing years. We avoid romantic relationships to stave off heartache and build a cage of loneliness in the process. We dream of starting a business "one day" and while away our time in a thankless profession that kills our passion for the very work we used to love. You're not as safe as you think. Unpleasant things are going to happen to you; it's an inevitability. So stop pretending like life can be lived in a room with padded walls. Bad things may happen, but if they do, it should be along the path to a life fully experienced and not through your own misguided self-sabotage. There's a remarkable freedom in accepting the ubiquity of imperfection. It's a realization that might just save your life.

LIVED LEARNING

Human nature is to worry about huge but unlikely threats, such as a terrorist attack and ignore more quotidian dangers like the hamburger you're eating as you read this. What is one unsexy but significant risk you've been overlooking in your own life? How might you take steps today to start to manage that risk?

Consider something you've always wanted to do but have been too terrified to try thus far. Have you locked yourself inside a cage of your own self-justifying excuses? What's one small step you could take today in the direction of that dream?

CHAPTER SIX

YOUR IDEAS AREN'T ALL THAT ORIGINAL

Let's talk aliens (just when you thought this book couldn't get any weirder, right?). Whether or not aliens exist is certainly beyond the scope of this book, (if you ask my Mom, she swears she's seen a UFO, but then again we ARE from Alabama so it's kind of par for the course) but I would like to briefly touch on alien spacecraft. How do we refer to an alien spacecraft in colloquial terms?

We call it a flying saucer.

Now, whether or not you believe in UFO's or not is of no concern to me. However, it is interesting that we take what is presumably one of the most advanced pieces of machinery in the known galaxy and name it after a dinner plate. The dish on which you place your teacup and a Martian vehicle are given rough equivalence! This tendency to describe the new and unknown in terms of the familiar has a rich history and is reflective of the ways in which we form new ideas.

The term "iron horse" was used to refer to locomotives in the 1820's and 30's at a time when horses still powered most machinery. When trains came onto the scene, many people were unaware of what they were and how they worked, so it made sense to compare them to the prevailing power source of the day, while making a differentiating note of their metallic composition. The naming rubric used to coin terms like "iron horse" and "flying saucer" belies what modern research tells us about the ways in which new ideas are born – they come from a combination of things we already know and are born by human contact.

IDEAS ARE REPRODUCTIVE

We tend to think of idea creation as sterile, asexual and hard to manage. We assume that great ideas spring forth, fully formed into the minds of geniuses who bear little resemblance to you or I. Eureka moments are created ex nihilo, usually in strange places like the shower. Our tendency to construe ideas thusly positions them in much the same realm as giftedness – you either get a good idea or you don't, but you can't force the issue. This wrongheaded notion about where ideas come from is doubly damning; we are misinformed about the wellspring of creativity and are thus discouraged from doing what it takes to have better ideas. You see, new ideas don't just spring up from nowhere, they are created when two old ideas well, you know….ahem, do it.

Steven Johnson, author of WHERE GOOD IDEAS COME FROM: THE NATURAL HISTORY OF INNOVATION spent five years studying the genesis of some of the world's greatest ideas. In his research, he found that big bold ideas are a. usually formed over a series of years (a process he calls a "slow hunch" and b. typically occur when two "partial hunches" collide. Dispelling the notion that ideas are housed in the minds of people of singular genius, Johnson posits that a lot of the time we have part of the answer and are not able to arrive at a more complete answer until we interface with people who have another piece of the puzzle.[XLII]

Part of the reason that our ideas just aren't that great is that my idea needs yours and vice versa.

Johnson's research into idea generation begins to paint a picture of how we can cultivate better thoughts ourselves. First, we have to be patient. Even when it seems as though a "Eureka!" moment has occurred, the idea has typically been simmering, partially formed, for a number of years. Second, we need to interface with other people and ideas that are outside of our own areas of expertise. Johnson cites the coffeehouses of Enlightenment Era Europe as a huge boon for the explosion of thought leadership during that period. People who had heretofore been meeting in pubs (and therefore not possessed of all their faculties) were now meeting in places where they could imbibe a non-alcoholic beverage and share their views. Of course, the flipside of this is that if we are not filling our heads with new and varied information, we are unlikely to arrive at any great truths, since there is a strong likelihood that the information we are missing resides elsewhere.

EVERYTHING IS A REMIX

We are currently living in what is referred to as a "Remix Culture"; a culture that favors creating new works through the creation of extant, derivative works. The debate continues to rage about the legality of remixing others' works, but it also begs the question, "Are we capable of original thought?"

As we noted previously, the world of humanities has beat the world of science to the punch. We read in Ecclisiastes 1:9, "The thing that has been, it is that which shall be; and that which is done is that which shall be done: and there is no new thing under the sun." Channeling a similar notion, Sir Isaac Newton famously said that "We are like dwarfs sitting on the shoulders of giants. We see more, and things that are more distant, than they, but because they raise us up, and by their great stature add to ours."[XLIII]

Perhaps the most concise and enjoyable explication of the collaborative and derivative nature of idea creation is Kirby Ferguson's excellent four part web video series, "Everything is a Remix."[XLIV] Drawing on well known examples from popular media, Ferguson brings to life Steven Johnson's notion that new ideas are born when old ideas come together. Even more importantly, he makes the point that we all become facile in our various areas of study by mimicking the work of others. Eventually, once we have mastered the "classics", we become fluent in the language of whatever it is we are learning and can create new ideas by riffing on old ones.

Consider the following; of the 10 highest grossing films from the past 10 years, 74 of 100 are either sequels or remakes. Even seminal, genre-defining films such as "Star Wars" are really little more than a patchwork quilt of other, older ideas that influenced their creators. For example:

1.The basic framework of "Star Wars" is built around Joseph Campbell's idea of a "monomyth" as found in his groundbreaking work on heroic archetypes, "The Hero with a Thousand Faces." This outline features elements such as the "call to adventure," "supernatural aid," "the belly of the whale," and "the road of trials," all of which feature prominently in the "Star Wars" narrative.

2.The iconic opening of the Star Wars movies (moving text fading slowly into a starry background) was lifted directly from the Flash Gordon serials of the 30's.

3. The work of Japanese director Akira Kurosawa is also heavily borrowed from in the Lucas films. Kurosawa's influence can be seen in the presence of masters of spiritual swordplay, a bickering duo (RJD2 and C3PO), a subterranean hideaway and boastful bad guys who lose an arm in battle with the weapon still clutched tight.

The similarities don't stop there though. In many cases, scenes from previous films were taken and used to storyboard the actual sequence in the Lucas film. For instance:

★ The scene where Luke Skywalker discovers his slaughtered family is reminiscent of a scene from "The Searchers", a 1956 John Wayne movie.

★ The attack on the Death Star is cobbled together from a series of influences including "The Dambusters", "633 Squadron", and "The Bridges at Toko-Ri."

★ C3PO bears a striking resemblance to tin woman in the classic film "Metropolis."

★ A number of the space shots were inspired by the film school class, "2001: A Space Odyssey."

★ The shots of Luke Skywalker swinging on ropes with Princess Laia are carbon copies of similar shots in "The 7th Voyage of Sinbad" and "Tarzan."

None of this is to take a thing away from George Lucas, who is clearly a brilliant artist. Indeed, the timelessness of Star Wars is a testament to its greatness. What it does illustrate however, is that even geniuses like George Lucas create new genres by cobbling together old ones. Lucas' genius is not in having dreamt up something wholly new, it is in having seamlessly combined old memes into something qualitatively different than the sum of its parts. George Lucas was able to do this because he was a student of the old masters. He studied the filmmakers that went before him and by synthesizing and remixing their ideas, was able to create something all his own. As Ferguson says in "Everything is a Remix", "Creation requires influence."

THE NEED FOR MIMICRY

Hopefully we have begun to dispel the myth of great ideas being the non-effortful birthright of the chosen few. But we still need to delve more deeply into just how great ideas become, well, great. The first steps in that process are remarkably unsexy and require, of all things, copying. Consider a few of the following examples culled from Ferguson's above-mentioned research.

* Bob Dylan's first album contained eleven cover songs.

* Richard Pryor began what would eventually be a groundbreaking comedy career doing an act that was little more than a Bill Cosby ripoff.

* Hunter S. Thompson retyped the entire "Great Gatsby" to simply get the feel of writing a great novel.

Imitation is the means by which we become masterful in our chosen domain and it is only once we have mastered the fundamentals through copying that we are able to create our own works of genius. We master our chosen domain by replicating old ideas and in so doing, put ourselves in a position to create new permutations of those ideas. Contrary to popular belief, Thomas Edison did not invent the lightbulb. What he did do was improve upon the idea, after over six thousand failed iterations, until he arrived at the first commercially viable model.

Similarly, Henry Ford is often credited with being the "Father of the Automobile" and having invented the assembly line, both of which are simply not true. The assembly line was invented 1867, interchangeable parts in 1801 and the automobile in 1885. But it was not until 1908 that Henry Ford was able to combine all of the above elements to create the world's first mass-produced car, the famous Model T.

Combinatorial ideas also gave birth to the internet, the printing press and the personal computer, to name but a few. Just ask Mark Zuckerberg, who arrived late to the social media party but created a social networking site now approaching a billion users. True innovation is less about being first to market and more about improving upon an existing idea until it goes viral.

GARBAGE IN...

Hopefully by now I have dispelled the notion of idea creation as a passive, asexual thing that is out of your control. Simply understood, having great ideas involves exposing yourself to ideas, mastering those concepts, and then tweaking them to create original works. Sounds easy, right? Well, yes, theoretically. On paper, we are better positioned than ever before to be exposed to the foundational ideas whose mastery could lead us to make grand schemes of our own. After all, the internet provides the average American with worlds of knowledge unavailable to kings in the not too distant past. We now create a greater volume of content every three days than we did in the 2000 years previous (I'll stop and let you read that one more time). Technology gives us staggering access to knowledge, but how are we using it?

To answer that question, I'd like to familiarize you with a few numbers – 27, 42, 80 and 9 million.

27 – is the percentage of Americans who graduate with a four-year college degree.[XLV] 42 – is the percentage of those college graduates who go on to never read another book again after college. 80 is the percentage of American households that do not purchase a single book within the space of a year. 9 million is the viewership of "The Jersey Shore", a sex and booze filled romp through the inconsequential lives of a group of Garden State nobodies whose notable accomplishments include their catch phrase "GTL" (gym, tan, laundry – the only three activities in which they regularly engage).[XLVI]

And while the vast majority of Americans don't buy a book in any given year, the average US household has 2.24 TV's that stay on an average of almost seven hours a day (6 hours and 47 minutes to be exact)! The A.C. Nielsen company estimates that the average individual watches 4 hours of TV a day, which works out to 2 months of non-stop TV watching within any given year. Assuming an average life expectancy of 80 years, Joe and Jane American will have spent 9 hours of their life watching television.

The tools we have for spreading knowledge are only as good as the ways in which we interact with them. We have unprecedented access to knowledge, which could conceivably expedite the process of mastery and exposure to "half ideas" that lead to breakthroughs. But at the time of publication, the most followed Twitter accounts are Lady Gaga, Justin Bieber, Katy Perry, Shakira, Rihanna, Kim Kardashian and Britney Spears. Technology and social media are powerful no doubt, but we will determine whether they are powerful for good or ill. Technology can hasten the spread of great new ideas are can be a megaphone for inanity. You determine each and every day how you will use these powerful tools and whether or not they will ultimately lead you to have any great new ideas.

THE PATH FORWARD

I've got some good news and some bad news. Bad news first you say? Ok. So, it looks like your ideas aren't all that original. Instead, they are an amalgamation of a bunch of other junk that's floating around in your head (and the heads of those around you). That said, there are still a few things you can do to ensure that your ideas and thoughts remain as vibrant and novel as possible.

Expose Yourself to Great Media – TV, mobile devices, the internet have all expedited the delivery of information, not to mention unfettered access. And what have we done with this wealth of information? Well, watch cat videos mostly. It's not that any of these mediums are inherently a time suck (as we so often view them). It's just that we use them in vapid and wasteful ways. Use the ubiquity of technology to expose yourself to new ideas, different approaches to living as well as to brush up on the classics. Humans are built for empathy and as we begin to view different ways of approaching the world, we start to consider the merits and demerits of our own worldview relative to theirs. We can learn a great deal without ever leaving the couch, if we'd only just turn off the "Real Housewives of Atlanta."

Surround Yourself With Smarties – Jim Rohn famously said that, "You are the average of the five people you spend the most time with."[XLVII] While the specific number may be arbitrary, there is no denying that we can be buoyed up or beaten down by the company we keep in terms of our ability to expand our thinking. All too often, I see executives surround themselves with doofuses to enhance their own brilliance by contrast. This is not so far removed from the tactic employed by single folks everywhere of selecting wingmen that are less physically attractive. It may work at a bar but it won't work here – choose someone smarter than you and let the gap you perceive between your intelligence and theirs push you on to bigger and better things.

Being surrounded by smart folks is a good start, but it's just a start. They not only need to be smart, they need to be smart in different ways than you. It is a tactic of lesser lights is to select a cadre of yes people to create an illusion of consensus around all of their great ideas. While this feels good in the short run, it's going to hurt like hell when this uniformity of thought leads you to create tired, uninspired products. Choose friends who see the world differently and thoughtfully consider their views relative to your own.

Finally, make sure these smarties have the mouth to match. All the smarts and creativity in the world are of no use if they lie fallow in the mind of your friend. Not only should they be smarter and think differently than you, they should be free with sharing their opinions. Read Patrick Lencioni's fervent cries for "unfiltered dialogue"[XLVIII] or listen to Steve Johnson talk about the collision of divergent opinions to form great new ideas. Real genius is brought to life when people with differing ideas have vigorous discussion undergird by mutual respect, if any of the three points above are lacking, this will be impossible.

Many folks see a friend as a cheerleader, someone to pick you up when the world has kicked you into the gutter. While this is certainly icing on the cake, it's far less crucial. God gave you a Mommy to cut out your press clippings. A friend is someone that cares enough about you to tell you when your ideas suck.

Be Generative — Filling your head with good ideas is the easy part — taking those vague notions and making them something new and bigger is where the rubber meets the road. For many of us, learning is its own reward. It's enjoyable, it makes your more interesting and it enriches your life in countless ways. However, learning without application is intellectual masturbation.

Mastering a skill set and then rehashing it ad nauseum gives a semblance of proficiency without any actual growth. Truly great people are always seeking to learn that next thing, to take that next step into the unknown. They realize that only by always being slightly uncomfortable with your current levels of skill and understanding will you ever become the best in the world at what you do. So, take all that great stuff you know and put it to work. Some of it will hold up to the fire of experience and some of it will vaporize. But that's cool — "all these things shall be for thy experience" as the saying goes.

LIVED LEARNING

Choose three books that you've always wanted to read (or that would deepen your understanding of some desired content area) and purchase them today. Right now. Seriously…go ahead. Now, choose a date three months from now by which you will have read all the books. Determine a reward for reading them in time as well as a punishment for not having read them and make it known to someone you trust who will hold you to your goal.

Create a forum for sharing your big ideas. Since your brain and the information you've filled it with are one of a kind, so will your ideas be unique. Choose a forum for sharing your thoughts, whether it be a blog, podcast, book or whatever else. Don't be stingy with your genius and you just might set in motion a flood of genius as others bump up against your views of the world.

CHAPTER SEVEN

YOU'RE CHASING THE WRONG DREAM

I want you to consider the following categories in terms of how much you value them as part of living a meaningful life. Assign a point value to each of them so that they total to one hundred. If it helps, you might imagine a pie chart with a larger piece of the pie signifying something that is of greater value to you.

VALUES:

Family –

Health –

Wealth –

Spirituality –

Intellectual Growth –

Total: 100

Now I'd like you to consider what percentage of your average day or week is spent in pursuit of each of these goals. Assuming a 16-hour day, if you consistently spend two hours a day reading and learning new things, you would assign a value of 12.5 to "Intellectual Growth" (since 2/16 = 12.5) and so forth. Go ahead and do that now.

BEHAVIORS:

Family –

Health –

Wealth –

Spirituality –

Intellectual Growth –

Total: 100

Compare your stated values with the way you actually spend your time. Any surprises? If you're like most people you probably noticed some startling discrepancies between the person you'd like to be and the person you are. After all, you vote with your time and behavior is a much better predictor of who you're becoming than are your values. So why are we so hypocritical with ourselves?

Part of the answer is born of necessity. The 40 + hour workweek is a cultural norm that is a vestige of the industrial era. Although it has little relevance (I would argue) in the new knowledge and service economy, the fact is, if you work for someone else you're likely to have an 8 to 5 schedule. This reality, paired with an ever-more-sprawling American landscape and the omnipresence of cellular devices, means that we spend a lot of time working, getting to work, or communicating with work.

But a second, bigger reason we become so ensconced in our work is that we think that making money is the shortcut to a happy, meaningful life.

All of the things we profess to value more than money take a backseat to making a buck, since we assume that the latter will facilitate the former. We'll have time for prayer and meditation once we don't have to grind out a living. We'll spend time with the family when we can finally afford to take them somewhere nice on vacation and we'll start working out once the busy season is over. All the things that would truly make us happy get put on hold as we labor under the notion that money will make it all right. Research shows that nothing could be further from the truth.

KEEPING UP WITH THE JONESES

We're all familiar with the term "keeping up with the Joneses" but it's doubtful that we understand just how deeply ingrained this is in our concept of wealth and success. Each year, a Gallup poll asks Americans to determine "What is the smallest amount of money a family of four needs to get along in this community?" Gallup finds that the answers to this question moves up in line with average incomes of the respondents. In a developed country like ours, the notions of "relative wealth" and "relative poverty" are very much at play.[XLIX]

No doubt there is true hunger, poverty and want that does go on in our country, and that is not to be minimized. But among the middle and upper socio-economic classes, people tend to look to others to determine whether or not they are successful rather than pointing to some static measure of wealth. Studies show that the most noticeable way in which money impacts happiness is negatively! We see that the very rich enjoy a slight bump in happiness given their comparative superiority, but the "have nots" are made absolutely miserable as they look up at their better resourced counterparts. Given that the increase in happiness is slight and that the rich make up a small fraction of the total population, in general, the tendency to view money in comparative terms is the source of a great deal of woe.

Given our tendency to compare our own incomes with what others have, we only feel better off if we move up relative to those with whom we compare ourselves. Thinking of wealth creation in this comparative light, it becomes a contest where your gains are tantamount to my losses and vice versa. In this paradigm, my striving for a greater income and working longer hours has decreased your happiness in aggregate. In a very real sense, we are attempting to climb to the top of the corporate ladder on the backs of those with whom we interact, and in so doing, we are sacrificing a great deal of what would really make us happy along the way. Given this human tendency to compare and construe wealth in relative terms, it's easy to see how the work/life balance we are constantly striving to achieve continues to shift increasingly toward work. After all, if we take a break, the people with whom we are comparing ourselves will be that much further ahead in the race upon our return. As long as work remains a "You win, I lose" scenario, our relationship with our fellowman will be strained at best as we continue to push each other in the direction of greater and greater imbalance.

The American tendency toward outward displays of wealth and comparative measurement is not endemic to all developed countries. Switzerland is just one example of a very wealthy country with a diametrically opposed philosophy relative to showy wealth. As opposed to the American mantra of, "If you've got it, flaunt it" the Swiss take an "If you've got it, hide it" approach so as not to provoke envy in others. The Swiss approach demonstrates that our views are an outcropping of a specific way of viewing wealth rather than something fundamental about human nature. It is up to us to determine to support each other on the way to balance and true happiness rather than prodding each other toward jealousy and excess.

I'LL STOP WHEN...

Another self-delusional variant of chasing money for happiness is the "I'll stop slaving away at work when I reach xyz number." Your magic number may be a salary figure ("If I could just make $??? I'd be happy") or it may be a wished for dollar amount to have in the bank. But, whatever it is, I can promise you that when you get there, it won't seem like enough. You see, we are not conditioned to think of money in terms of "enough," as one of my clients once said to me, "Doc, you can never be too rich or too skinny."

The scientific name for this phenomenon is the "hedonic treadmill" or "hedonic adaptation", referring to the fact that we must make more and more money to keep our level of happiness in the same place. What tends to happen is that our expectations rise and fall with our earnings (as well as other circumstances in our life), keeping our happiness at a relatively stable place. To demonstrate this effect, I'd like for you to consider two groups, that seemingly have little in common – paraplegics and lottery winners.

We would hypothesize that one year after the life changing event, lottery winners would be much happier and paraplegics would be much sadder, right? But this is simply not the case. One year after their respective events, it makes little difference whether you are riding in a Bentley or a wheelchair – happiness levels remain relatively static.[LI] Why? We tend to overpredict the impact of external events on our happiness. One year later, paraplegics have found out their accidents were not as catastrophic as they may have feared and have coped accordingly. Similarly, lottery winners have found out that having money brings with it a variety of complications. No amount of spending can take away some of the tough things life throws at each and every one of us. As the saying goes, "wherever you go, there you are." In much the same way, we tend to project forward to a hypothesized happier time, when we have more money in the bank or are making a bigger salary. The fact of the matter is, when that day arrives, we are unlikely to recognize it and will simply project forward once again, hoping in vain that something outside of ourselves will come and make it all better.

A recent Princeton study set out to answer the age-old question, "Can money buy happiness?" Their answer? Sort of.[LII] Researchers found that making little money did not cause sadness in and of itself but it did tend to heighten and exacerbate existing worries. For instance, among people who were divorced, 51% of those who made less than $1,000/month reported having felt sad or stressed the previous day, whereas that number fell to 24% among those earning more than $3,000/month. Having more money seems to provide those undergoing adversity with greater security and resources for dealing with their troubles. However, the researchers found that this effect (mitigating the impact of difficulty) disappears altogether at $75,000. For those making more than $75,000 individual differences have much more to do with happiness than does money. While the study does not make any specific inferences as to why $75,000 is the magic number, I'd like to take a stab at it. For most families making $75,000/year, they have enough to live in a safe home, attend quality schools and have appropriate leisure time. Once these basic needs are met, quality of life has less to do with buying happiness and more to do with individual attitudes. After all, someone who makes $750,000 can buy a faster car than someone who makes $75,000, but their ability to get from point A to point B is not substantially improved. It would seem that once we have our basic financial needs met, the rest is up to us.

YOU'RE CHASING THE WRONG DREAM

We've discussed that happiness does not come from chasing money or even hitting the lottery, (and conversely that sadness is not borne of personal tragedy) so what does make us happy? Well, fortunately or unfortunately (depending on how well-adjusted your parents are), a great deal of happiness comes from our "hedonic set point" which is genetically determined. A 10-year, longitudinal study of 1,093 identical twins found that between 44 and 52% of subjective wellbeing is accounted for by genetic factors.[LIII] So, roughly half of what makes you happy is out of your control, sorry to say.

But what about the part that we can control? Of the remaining 50%, roughly 10% is due to external circumstances and a whopping 40% is due to intentional activities, or the choices we make. We discussed before how we tend to overrate the importance of the things that happen to us, and sure enough, only 10% of what makes us happy is accounted for by lucky and unlucky breaks. 80% of the non-genetic components of happiness can be controlled by our attitude and by making choices that are consistent with finding true joy. And the first step in this pursuit is ensuring that the goals we are setting for ourselves are consistent with finding true happiness.

If 80% of the happiness that is in our control comes from setting and working toward positive goals, what sort of goals should we be setting? Heady[LIV] (year?) has found that goals focused on enriching relationships and social resources are likely to increase wellbeing. We connect with a number of close friends and find joy within those relationships.

On the other hand, he found that goals based around monetary achievement have a negative effect on overall wellbeing. Unlike friendship, which we "consume" in limited but satisfying quantities, we feel as though we can never really reach a financial goal. Having a core group of close friends sates us; it is sufficient to meet our social needs and we do not pine for ever-greater numbers of friends. Not so with financial goals, just as we reach our former goal, the hedonic treadmill kicks in and our excitement over having "arrived" gone in an instant. Dr. Daniel Gilbert, a happiness expert at Harvard says that pursuing wealth at the expense of more satisfying goals has a high opportunity cost. "When people spend their effort pursuing material goods in the belief that they will bring happiness, they're ignoring other, more effective routes to happiness."[LV] The simple fact is this: chasing money and material goods is an itch that our flawed psychology will never let us scratch.

A WISH BEFORE DYING

Bronnie Ware is an Australian nurse who has spent her career in a palliative care unit, caring for those with very little time to live. As someone who interacts with the dying, she has had the privilege of speaking with these people at the things that make their life worth living, as well as what they wish they'd done differently. Ms. Ware summarized the top five regrets of those about to pass on in her excellent blog, "Inspiration and Chai." The "Top Five Regrets of the Dying" are:[LVI]

1. I wish I'd had the courage to live a life true to myself, not the life others expected of me.

2. I wish I hadn't worked so hard.

3. I wish I'd had the courage to express my feelings.

4. I wish I had stayed in touch with my friends.

5. I wish I had let myself be happier.

Notice, not one mention of money and the only mention of work is to say that (especially male patients) had done less of it. If your values vs. behavior chart looks like I think it does, you are chasing the wrong dream and setting the wrong goals. As you sit and evaluate your life as it draws to a close, I promise you that you will never regret the money you didn't make, but you may well regret lost time spent chasing a counterfeit notion of happiness.

THE PATH FORWARD

In a money-obsessed world that has socialized us to chase the almighty dollar, it can be weirdly unsettling to learn that money isn't everything. As much as we whine about money, having something that is the physical embodiment of happiness is nice. We can hold it, save it, get more of it, all while mistakenly thinking that getting paid is how we "arrive." Realizing that money does not directly equate to meaning can leave us with a sense of groundlessness but once we've stripped away that faulty foundation, we are able to replace it with things that lead to less evanescent feelings of happiness. Breaking your overreliance on money as a substitute for real joy is a great first step, here are some ways to move forward upon having made this important realization.

Spend money in ways that matter – Let's be balanced in the way we talk about and think about money. It's not the key to happiness, but it's not nothing either. A lot of our troubles with money stem from the way we spend it. We think that buying "things" will make us happy. We engage in retail therapy which is quickly followed by feelings of regret at being overextended. Before we know it, we're surrounded the relics of our discontent; the things we bought to be happy become constant reminders that we're not.

Instead of amassing a museum of junk – spend your money on things of real value. Spend a little more on quality, healthy food and take the time to savor your new purchases. Use your money to invest in a dream – pay yourself to take a little time off and write that novel about which you've always dreamt. Give charitably and experience the joy of watching those less fortunate benefit from your wealth. Finally, spend money on having special experiences with your loved ones. It's true that money doesn't buy happiness, but it can do a great deal to facilitate it if you approach it correctly.

Find a new metric – Part of the appeal of money as a barometer for happiness is that it's so…well…quantifiable. Meaning, joy, happiness, fulfillment are all abstractions that can be hard to get our hands around. Thus, we aim for something we can count (but end up sadly disappointed). So, take things that really will make you happy and try to come up with metrics for those things instead. Maybe you enjoy painting and you could set a goal to complete three new pieces by the end of the summer. Perhaps you want to be more service oriented and you could set a goal to engage in a charitable act each week. The impulse to measure happiness is a natural and good one, let's just make sure we're using a yardstick that delivers on its promises.

LIVED LEARNING

Determine three times in your life when you were truly joyful – not happy so much as deeply contented. What role (if any) did money play in those moments? What lessons can these moments teach you about how to best spend money to live a great life?

We talked early in the chapter about the imbalance in what we profess to love versus how we spend our time. What is one thing you value that you are largely ignoring right now? How might you spend more time focusing on this at the expense of something that matters less in the long run?

CHAPTER EIGHT

THE TIME WILL NEVER BE RIGHT

Consider something you've always wanted to do but that you've put off doing because it scares you. In fact, just think of something you'd eventually like to do but haven't yet, since you may not even be aware of all of your reasons for not having embarked on that journey just yet. Maybe that something is having a child. Maybe it's starting a business. Or perhaps it's writing a book, getting serious with a romantic partner, or any number of other aspirations you've yet to reach. Let's say for discussion's sake that the thing you are considering is starting a business. You ask yourself...

"Should I or shouldn't I start a business?"

Easy enough, right? You make a t-chart, list the pros and cons and then make a decision! Well, let's examine how you go about dissecting this question. You do your best to dispassionately weigh the pros and perils, but if you're like most folks (and you are, remember, you're not special) there is a flaw in the system. Drawing on his background in evolutionary psychology, James Friedrich has come to the conclusion that as we evaluate important decision in our life, our primary aim is to avoid the most costly errors. That is, we make decisions that make us "not unhappy" rather than "blissful." We want to be "not broke" more than we want to live abundantly. To use some familiar Internet colloquialisms, we choose a sure "meh" over a possible "woot!" To use the above-mentioned example, you're far more likely to focus on the potential perils of failing at business than you are the happiness and freedom that might accrue to you.

The evolutionary roots of this system of self-preservation make sense. It was not all that long ago (in terms of evolutionary time) that our forebears were called upon daily to make life and death decisions. For people living on the savannahs of Africa, choosing to zig when you should have zagged could spell the end. Historically, decision-making has been very wrapped up in preserving physical safety and ensuring that physical needs were met. In this life-and-death scenario, minimizing risk at the expense of self-actualization is only logical. However, in the intervening millennia, things have changed and our thought patterns have not kept pace. At least in the US, we now live in a service economy that produces more ideas than it does "things." Fully 44% of US GDP is accounted for by financiers and others who do little but move money around. We have moved from an agrarian to an industrial to a knowledge-based economy and our ability to cope with personal stressors has not kept pace.

In the US and Western Europe, most people have the base of Maslow's pyramid met – they have adequate food, water, sleep and safety. Having now met these basic needs, they are left to wrangle with more metaphysical concerns such as belonging and self-actualization. No writer has expressed this existential struggle more succinctly and beautifully than Chuck Palahniuk, who said, through his character Tyler Durden,

"We're the middle children of history, man. No purpose or place. We have no Great War. No Great Depression. Our great war is a spiritual war. Our great depression is our lives."[LVII]

What we are left with is a brain and a decision-making modality that is ill suited for our modern milieu. We are programmed to choose safety, even at the expense of joy, in an environment where safety abounds and joy is hard to find. Numerous studies have shown that people are twice as upset about a loss as they are pleased about a gain (just ask my Dad the stockbroker if he gets as many calls when the market is up as he does when it's down). Unless we learn to train our brains to evaluate risk and reward on a more even keel, we will remain trapped in a life of risk-aversion that keeps us from taking the very risks that might make us happy.

TRAIN UP A CHILD

Let's say you and your significant other are headed out for a night on the town. You're looking for a trustworthy sitter for your young child and have asked a close friend to describe two potential childcare professionals for the evening. Your friend gives you the following descriptions and you must choose one of the two.

Sitter One – Is described as intelligent, industrious, impulsive, critical, stubborn, and envious.

Sitter Two – Is described as envious, stubborn, critical, impulsive, industrious and intelligent.

So, proud mama or papa – which do you choose? Well, you being the bright, special person that you are, you've likely figured out that the two lists of adjectives are identical. Odds are though; you had a strong gut reaction that the first sitter is more desirable. This is due to something called the "irrational primacy effect" or the tendency to give greater weight to information that comes earlier in a list or sentence. It turns out that what's true of communication is also true of our lives – the lessons that we learn early in life are same of the most lasting.

As the parent of a two-year old, I can personally attest to the amount of time I spend saying "No" and trying to protect my child from things that are scary, dangerous, sugary or generally bad for her. And while this may be developmentally appropriate early in life (she always has had a thing for electrical sockets!) it becomes less so as the child learns, grows and matures. Notwithstanding this growth, many parents persist in limiting their child's exploration, ostensibly to protect them but sometimes more realistically as a protection against damaging their own ego.

Adam Sandler's "They're All Going to Laugh at You"[LVIII] bit from his first comedy CD parodies (in addition to the horror film "Carrie") the parental tendency to overprotect.

Kid: "Hey mom, I gotta get up pretty early tomorrow for Little League try-outs."

Mom: "NOOO!!"

Kid: "Yeah, I have to be at the field at 9 o'clock..."

Mom: "They're all gonna laugh at you!"

Kid: "Do you think you could drop me off there?..."

Mom: "They're all gonna laugh at you!"

Kid: "How am I gonna get there?"

Mom: "They're all gonna laugh at you!"

Kid: "I'll walk I guess."

Mom: "NOOO!!"

While Sandler's delivery is certainly over the top, I think that most of us recognize the parental urge to protect as well as the childlike desire to be protected. Sometimes, unwittingly, we can smother the people we love by keeping them out of the game so to speak. We understand that risk brings with it the potential of hurt and we don't want those we love to suffer. We are raised this way, learn to conflate risk aversion with love and pass that same ethic on to the next generation. "Go into accounting (or nursing, or whatever)" we say, "that's a steady work." "Don't study art" we opine, "what are you going to do with that?" In this way, we project our own fear of loss onto others, and inadvertently encourage others to sabotage their true happiness in the name of security.

THE DEVIL THAT YOU KNOW

By now, we are all at least somewhat aware of the toll taken by alcohol abuse. Notwithstanding our general awareness, the specific statistics are still staggering:

- This year 10, 389 people will die in drunk driving accidents[LIX]

- One in three people will be involved in an alcohol related crash in their lifetime[LX]

- One in five teens binge drink[LXI]

- Alcohol is commonly implicated in incidents of family violence[LXII]

Incest is twice as likely among daughters of alcoholics

We could go on of course, but even the few stats above paint a horrifying picture for the children and family members of alcoholics. So, why is it then that 50% of children of alcoholics go on to marry alcoholics themselves?[LXIII] On its face this sounds insane, given all the havoc wreaked by living with an alcoholic. And while this behavior is certainly maladaptive, it speaks directly to the very human need for certainty.

It is a truism that people want to know what they are getting into – even if it is boring, bad or unfulfilling. Pain researchers have found that expected pain is much less disruptive than unexpected pain, even if the painful stimulus delivered is exactly the same. Our brains are not well equipped to handle ambiguity. We jump to conclusions and hang on to our beliefs long after they have been objectively disproven, all in the spirit of knowing what we're working with. Simply put, we'd rather be doing the wrong thing than not know what we're doing.

Thus, we see children of alcoholics tending to marry alcoholics. After all, they are familiar with the coping strategies required to deal with an alcoholic and have a decent idea of what to expect day to day, even if what they are expecting isn't all that favorable. A similar dynamic is afoot when soldiers, psychologically scarred by the horrors of war, continue to reenlist. As averse as they may be to the things they have seen in the field, they have become acclimated to the hardships of soldiering whereas they may feel less equipped to say, raise a child or attend college. These seemingly counterintuitive approaches begin to look more lucid as we understand our deep-seated need for certainty. While it might not always make us happy, we do tend to go with "the devil that we know."

THE POWER OF
PERSONAL NARRATIVE

Let's look now at the net effect of our tendency to eschew risk and seek out predictability on the way we talk to ourselves. I know, I know, you're not crazy and you don't mumble to yourself all day. But the fact is, each of us is always crafting and refining a personal narrative; a story we tell ourselves about who we are and why we do the things we do. This narrative has a powerful impact on the decisions we make, and ultimately how happy and self-fulfilled we are as a result.

In our efforts to perceive ourselves as rational human beings, we tend to think that we are logical and astute decision makers. We think of ourselves as thoughtful and reasoned when choosing a certain path and resist the idea that we are led about by our emotions or (gasp!) unconscious factors. If we're so logical, what accounts for the following:

Diabetes, the 7th leading cause of death, has a 50% instance of non-compliance with treatment protocols.

Nearly 60% of male Chinese doctors smoke.

About 50% of the 2 billion prescriptions filled each year are not taken as directed.

In our minds, we assume that once people know something, they will act accordingly. After all, what are school, church and corporate trainings about? Teaching people and hoping that increased knowledge positively impacts behavior. The truth is, it's not nearly that clean or simple. We are irrational, emotional beings who often make decisions emotionally and then work backwards to try and layer a thin veneer of rationality over top. In other words, we do what we want or what comes naturally, and then work backwards to explain all the reasons why that decision made sense.

This tendency to reason backwards has profound implications for how we make decisions about whether or not now is the right time to follow our dreams. As we've discussed previously, left to our own devices we tend to orient toward safety, sameness and wanting to be correct. Let's think about these tendencies in terms of our initial question of whether or not we should start a business.

Is starting a business safe? Not by a long shot. Fact is, a majority of small businesses fail. Does it preserve the status quo? Inevitably the answer to this question is no as well. You'd be called on to do all manner of new and disruptive things, and with that comes the uncertainty that none of us seems to like. Will it maximize our perceived competence? Undoubtedly not. Small business owners have to do it all – from billing to marketing to sales to execution. No one can be truly expert at all of those competency areas and the results may be that others see you struggling or being less than your usual perfect self.

Again, remember that these discussions are probably not happening in your head explicitly, but you'd be foolish not to assume they are registering on some level. If you admitted all of the above, you'd sound simultaneously pompous and scared, so you reason backwards to come up with a more rational sounding excuse. Maybe it's, "I'll get around to it when the economy picks up" or perhaps you of the "When I get a little more in savings" variety. Reasons like this are the sort that seemingly clear-thinking adults come up with, but the fact remains that you have just gilded over your underlying fears. Until you address the fear that undergirds you're ostensibly rational reasons for disengaging, you will never get any closer to living the life you've dreamed of.

MAKE YOUR OWN TIMING

Pop quiz! What do Disney, MTV, Chevrolet, Trader Joes, FedEx, CNN, Sports Illustrated, Microsoft, and Hewlett Packer all have in common? They were all started in a recession or a depression. Exceptional people do great things, even when the chips are stacked against them. A belief in your ability to rise above your circumstances is essential to all successes in life and keeps you from falling back on tired excuses about "I'll do X when Y happens." The leaders of the organizations listed above did not fall back on lazy reasoning masquerading as logic, they just did it.

Psychologists call this belief in personal self-efficacy having an "internal locus of control." People with an internal locus of control know that they can make choices and exert influence on their environment just as surely as they are acted upon by their environment. They understand that situation is not destiny. Conversely, those with an "external locus of control" believe that their efficacy will be largely predicated on the circumstances in which they find themselves. They will be as good or as bad as the situation into which they are dropped. These folks are tossed about the on the waves of life and not surprisingly their business fail at a much higher rate than do those of their more responsible counterparts (45% failure to 7% respectively).[LXVII]

Think of it this way – if you are only as good as the cards life deals you – what use are you as a leader? Anyone can be tossed about by the waves of life; it takes talent to swim upstream. Overreliance on external cues for deciding how to live your life is a sure recipe for helplessness and despair. If you want to find reasons why doing something new will make you feel scared and incompetent, you're in luck – you'll always be able to find them.

You're wired to create personal narratives that keep you fat, happy and stupid and if that's what you want for your life, keep that cruise control button firmly locked down. People who are truly engaged with life know that the time will NEVER be right. They know that excuses will always be there for the taking and that they can construct an airtight story that few people will question. People won't question it, because they're telling themselves the same type of stories. Stories about how they can't do any differently, how external factors inhibit their success and the like.

The sad irony about this type of self talk is that in our efforts to create safety, we only end up securing our own demise. It goes without saying that no one likes to lose; in this sense our fear of loss is natural and can be protective at times. However, it can also be damaging at times when it distorts our view of the world or leads us to not even play the game.

I'd like for you to consider the most meaningful thing you have ever done. I'm not sure what it is, probably couldn't even get in the ballpark. What I would wager however, is that it took a measure of risk, uncertainty, and hard work to achieve. To strive for certainty is to doom oneself to mediocrity. The irony of obsessive loss aversion is that our worst fears become realized in our attempts to manage them. The only way to never risk heartbreak is to never love, but what could be more heartbreaking than that? The only way to never risk failing is to never try, but not trying is the greatest failure of all.

THE PATH FORWARD

Every day we struggle with our love hate relationship with empowerment. We want to feel empowered and potent but if we recognize our own power, we simultaneously take upon ourselves the burden of that, which is the need to do something great with it. Well, I've got good and bad news for you – you are powerful. You heard it here first so take your fingers out of your ears and run with it! Here are a few places to start:

Own your power – There are people that only you can reach, lessons only you can teach and things that only you can accomplish. There are also things you totally suck at. Determine your strengths by examining your past successes, speaking with friends and trusted colleagues. That's the fun part – here comes the hard part; realizing what you owe the world as a result of these gifts.

Share your power - If Spiderman has taught us anything it's that "with great power comes great responsibility." Once you have determined the ways in which you are powerful, you must also determine how to meet the attendant obligations. Maybe you are a gifted singer who could lift spirits by sharing her voice. It could be that you are a skilled entrepreneur who could profitably coach others as they embark on their own journeys into business ownership. Whatever you're good at, it's incumbent upon you to pay it forward and share that gift with the world. Can you imagine how much more rich our lives would be if everyone took this approach?

Control your self-talk– Many of us have gotten really exceptional at passing the buck, sometimes in ways so seemingly real that it scarcely registers as shirking responsibility. Inevitably, you have a list of fallback excuses of varying veracity – everything from the ways in which your family holds you back, to your upbringing, to your finances, to your dog having eaten your homework. People who get in the habit of letting themselves off do so internally and almost imperceptibly. It's as though there is a tape running in their head all the time that tells that all the reasons that "now isn't the time."

A big piece of being able to move forward with confidence is getting a hold of this tape and ripping out the stringy parts until it's a huge mess (I realize my younger readers will have no idea what I'm talking about here). Until you control the almost unconscious negative messages you are sending yourself, it will be difficult for you to make progress.

LIVED LEARNING

- It's no surprise that people who are not living their own dreams project dissatisfaction onto others who come to them with questions about the feasibility of theirs. What might surprise you is that sometimes we actively surround ourselves with these naysayers to insulate ourselves from having to take risks! After all, if we've been told no by those closest to us, we'd be justified in not taking the risk, right? Wrong. The best mentors balance risk and reward seamlessly – replace the "perma bears" in your life with someone a little more balanced.

- As we've discussed, we tend to be very scared of high profile but improbable risks and ignore more everyday risks that are much more likely to occur. Examine your own life and determine one risk you're ignoring because it's not "sexy" enough. Maybe it's your health. Perhaps it's not wearing your seatbelt. It could be that you've ignored your diet for too long. Whatever it is, recognize that vanilla but dangerous risk for what it is and start to address it today.

CONCLUSION

The longer I live, the more I realize how paradoxical life can be. Perhaps no paradox is more puzzling than this – the more we need to be special the less special we become. Most of us plan on having an extraordinary life – after all, no little kid dreams of being mediocre (I had a dream of being a corrupt cop for a time, but that had more to do with my affinity for doughnuts than anything else). But somewhere along the way, we experience disappointment and we start over thinking the whole "live a great life" thing. We start trying too hard. Worse yet, we start taking shortcuts.

As we've discussed, traditional notions of specialness are comparative in nature – a zero sum games that pits friend against friend and begs for unethical behavior. The problem is, as much as this game makes sense to us on some level, it is inherently unsatisfying. Pursuing specialness as an end unto itself is to run a race without a finish line. The fact is, arbitrary markers of greatness never satisfy – you don't have to watch too many episodes of "VH1 Behind the Music "to figure out that money, gold records and unlimited groupie sex don't satisfy in the way people thought they might. As we close out our time together, I'd like to present you with three truths for having a special life that may seem counterintuitive on their face.

SKIP YOUR GRADUATION

One of the most disappointing but educational days of my life was the day I received my Ph.D. A doctorate degree is something about which individuals are rightly proud. Attaining doctor status represents the highest in educational attainment – it's no wonder parents everywhere want their children to be (or at least to marry) a doctor or a lawyer. Having largely bought the hype about the transformative power of those three little letters behind one's name, I become more and more excited about the power and respect I'd experience as a newly minted Ph.D.

Now remember, I'm a psychologist and I should know much better than this, but if I'm being honest, I thought my life would be much different once I was credentialed. The day of my graduation and the days immediately following, I remember the disappointment I felt. I still had money troubles. I was still impatient with people I loved. I still felt inadequate to help some of the people that came to me looking for answers. In building a good life, as in practically everything else, there are no quick fixes.

We tend to "reify" things like a doctorate degree, that is, objectify it and make it more real and powerful than it truly is. Without question, the people I met in my program, the clients that taught me so much and the books that I read were all enormously powerful. The "special" moniker I received from having a different colored tassle on my graduation robe? Absolutely impotent. A degree doesn't transform someone anymore than money, marriage, having children or anything else does. True personal transformation happens in the spaces in between, not at the arbitrary finish lines we create for ourselves along the way.

How often have we wished away various stages of our life, wishing for a someday that was ultimately anticlimactic when it arrived. People who live truly special lives learn that truth and meaning can be found or created in every minute of every day. They live their lives today, understanding that "big moments" will come and go, but won't define their lives.

YOU SHOULDN'T TRY TO BE GREAT

In his seminal work 'Good to Great'[LXVIII], Jim Collins found that two things were necessary for truly great (Level 5 in Collins' vernacular) leaders: humility and a highly focused strength of will. Perhaps Collins' greatest contribution to leadership literature is having shot down the sexy, if fallacious, idea of leaders as larger-than-life and ostentatious. So, why is it that after such paradigm-shifting discoveries we are still so mired in mediocrity in terms of our corporate and political leadership? I think one of the biggest and most overlooked answers to this question lies in the way we pursue leadership.

To illustrate this point, consider the times in your life that you've been the happiest. Ever notice how elusive happiness is when you try to pursuit it? Well it turns out you have something in common with a famous utilitarian philosopher (your Mom must be so proud)! John Stuart Mill said, "Those are only happy who have their minds fixed on some object other than happiness. Aiming thus at something else, they find happiness along the way."[LXIX] Part of happiness is the effortlessness and lightness of being that accompanies it. So, when we try and try to be happy, we are necessarily running afoul of one of its fundamental features. Something very similar can be said of trying to be a special.

I, like Jim Collins, think that humility is a necessary attribute of a specialness. That said, when we take the mantle of greatness upon us in the "how-can-I-lead-these-little-people" sort of way, we've already failed! Those who aspire to leadership, who view themselves as leaders in the traditional sense, and who buy leadership books (GOTCHA!) because they are somehow elevated, have violated one of the fundamental tenets of specialness before even truly beginning the journey. And as any sailor can attest, going on a journey that begins with a miscalculation can land you way off course.

YOU ARE THE ANSWER

Given that our concept of what it means to be special is typically based on a vapid ideal, it can tend to seem distant and difficult to attain. After all, do you have any idea what a Bugatti Veyron costs? Since success can seem so alien, we are often of the mind that we need to warp and suppress our natural, more vanilla interests to get there from here. Rather than find success within our own social sphere, we may write off those closest to us as unhelpful in our climb to the top. Worse yet, we may actually come to view them as impediments to our success and distance ourselves from the very people who got us to where we are today.

A similar dissociation may take place with our interests and passions. We subvert what we truly love in favor of pursuing we find more important or lucrative. Sure, you love kids but nobody ever got famous by reading "The Giving Tree" and changing diapers. Sure, you have a passion for the written word but what about the people who will scoff at your English degree ("What ARE you going to do with THAT?").

Well, if you worry about these sorts of things, I've got two important questions for you that will be highly predictive of how happy and successful you will be at work and in life. The first question is, "Do you want to be the best in the world at what you do?"

Be honest with yourself, some people see work as a means to an end and there's nothing wrong with that. If your idea of the good life is working a predictable 9 to 5, taking sixty minute lunch breaks, and rushing home to watch "Dancing With the Stars", you can stop reading now and head back over to TMZ. com. I'll wait for you to leave…thanks for reading this far, I know how much it hurts your brain!

So, if you're still reading, I'll assume you have some desire to be great at what you do, perhaps even the best in the world. If so, my second question for you is, "Do you find your work meaningful?"

If you answered "yes" to Question 1 and "no" to Question 2, please walk into your bosses' office, hand in your resignation, find a small cardboard box, and begin packing your personal effects. Why is that you ask? Because, if you do not find your work meaningful, you will never be the best in the world at what you do.

I'm of the mind that the "why" of our work is at least as important as the "how." More specifically, I believe that the "why" is instrumental in driving the "how." The first reason that I think having a purpose to your work is so imperative is that it catalyzes the effort necessary to be great.

Malcolm Gladwell has my dream job. Namely, pursuing his varied intellectual interests, writing about them, having awesome hair, and making a gazillion dollars. His most recent work, "Outliers" touches on those folks who hang out on the far right extreme of the bell curve measuring success. Gladwell's question is, "Why do some people succeed while others never really reach their true potential?"

Spoiler Alert: Gladwell arrives at two remarkably unsexy conclusions: 1.) greatness requires hard work and 2.) even if you work hard, you still need to get lucky. It is the first conclusion, the necessity of hard work, that is so inextricably tied to meaning.

One of the most often-quoted findings of "Outliers" is what is referred to as the "10,000 hour rule."[LXX] Americans love a story of effortless, preternatural talent. We like to imagine our business heroes as geniuses, miles above the rest of us, that have million dollar ideas with the same regularity that we other Philistines eat at McDonalds.

Gladwell's book puts this enticing, if fallacious notion to bed once and for all. What he found to be true, of everyone from Bill Gates, to the Beatles, to violin virtuosos, was that all of them had put in at least 10,000 hours of hard work at honing their craft. And guess what was necessary to put in those long hours? A deeply felt sense that the work they were doing was meaningful and bigger than them or the task itself.

There are no magic shortcuts to the top. Despite our fondest dreams to the contrary, success has been, and always will be deeply rooted in the bedrock of hard work. There is however, some magic in the way that doing work that we find personally meaningful can make 10,000 hours seem like the blink of an eye.

So, I ask you again, "Do you want to be great?" If so, you'd better know why the way you're living matters to you, or you'd better start living differently.

SO...ARE YOU GREAT YET?

I started out this book by telling you that you weren't that great, and I meant it. The thing is, you can be great. Actually, you ought to be great. In fact, great is your default setting! You were born special; a person with natural gifts, strengths and even idiosyncracies that uniquely positioned you to live a life that would have a positive impact on those with whom you came in contact. But along the way, life happened and you began to bury those natural gifts in an effort to follow a homogenized vision of success.

You buried your differences and ridiculed others for theirs, hoping that in so doing you'd "arrive." You bought into a counterfeit notion of what it meant to be great, a notion based on insecurity. A notion rooted in hurting others to elevate yourself. And you tried it. And you felt nothing.

So, today, you're not that great, but it's not because there is no greatness within you. Living a great life is fundamentally about scraping away all of the bad lessons and fallacious visions of happiness you've been sold. It's about realizing that the less you need to be special, the more special you'll become. It's about realizing that greatness isn't achieved at the top of the mountain, but at every rest stop and slip up along the way. And most of all, it's about realizing that what makes you unique can't be bought, earned or accomplished. It can only be unearthed as you have the personal courage to admit that you're pretty average, and in so doing, put yourself on the path to becoming so much more. Greatness is your birthright, specialness is your equilibrium, now just stop trying so hard and go and get it.

Endnotes

[I] Kierkegaard, S., & Lowrie, W. (1968). Attack upon Christendom. Princeton, NJ: Princeton University Press.

[II] Rand, A. (1957). Atlas shrugged. New York, NY: Random House.

[III] Frankl, V. (2006). Man's search for meaning. Boston, MA: Beacon Press.

[IV] The Secret. (n.d.) Retrieved February 26, 2012, from http://en.wikipedia.org/wiki/The_Secret_(book)

Byrne, R. (2006). The Secret. Hillsboro, OR: Beyond Words Pubishing.

[V] Minsky, M. L. (1986). The society of mind. New York, NY: Simon and Schuster.

[VI] Plato. (1909-14) The apology, Phædo and Crito Vol. II, Part 1 (B. Jowett, Trans.) New York, NY: P.F. Collier & Son. (Original work published n.d.)

[VII] Branden, N. (2001). The psychology of self-esteem: A revolutionary approach to self-understanding that launched a new era in modern psychology. San Francisco, CA: Jossey-Bass.

VIII Bronson, P. (2007, February 11). How not to talk to your kids: The inverse power of praise. New York Magazine. Retrieved from http://nymag.com/news/features/27840/

IX Mueller, C.M., & Dweck, C.S. (1998). Praise for intelligence can undermine children's motivation and performance. Journal of Personality and Social Psychology, 75(1), 33-52.

X Dweck, C. (2007, November 28). The secret to raising smart kids. Scientific America. Retrieved from http://www.scientificamerican.com/article.cfm?id=the-secret-to-raising-smart-kids

XI Seligman, M. (1972, February). Learned helplessness. Annual Review of Medicine, 23, 407-412. doi: 10.1146/annurev.me.23.020172.002203

XII Wachtel, K. (2011, February 28). Bernie Madoff: "My notoriety impresses" the other inmates. Business Insider. Retrieved from http://articles.businessinsider.com/2011-02-28/wall_street/30078515_1_bernie-madoff-sociopath-banco-santander

XII Select quotes from Bernard Madoff. (2011, March 1). International Business Times. Retrieved from http://au.ibtimes.com/mobile/articles/20110301/117015.htm

XIV Terman, L. M. (1926). Mental and physical traits of a thousand gifted children. Vol. 1. Genetic studies of genius (2nd ed.). Stanford, CA: Stanford University Press.

XV Kaufman, S.B. (2009, September 9). The truth about the "termites": What do the results of Lewis Terman's famous study really demonstrate? Psychologytoday.com. Retrieved from http://www.psychologytoday.com/blog/beautiful-minds/200909/the-truth-about-the-termites

[XVI] Saxon, W. (1989, August 14). On this day: William B. Shockley, 79, creator of transistor and theory on race. New York Times. Retrieved from http://www.nytimes.com/learning/general/onthisday/bday/0213.html

[XVII] Ekberg, M. (2007). The old eugenics and the new genetics compared. Social History of Medicine, 20(3), 581-593.

[XVII] Barnhardt, S. (2003). Eliminating barriers: Stigma statistics. Presentation to the Eliminating Barriers Statewide Stakeholders Meeting, August 27, 2003. Raleigh, NC.

[XIX] The National Organization on Disability. (1991). 1991 NOD survey of public attitudes toward people with disabilities [Data file]. Retrieved from http://www.socio.com/rad07.php

[XX] Lamy, R. E. (1996). Social consequences of mental illness. Journal of Consulting and Clinical Psychology, 30, 450-455.

[XXI] Sayce, L. (2000). From psychiatric patient to citizen: Overcoming discrimination and social exclusion. NY, New York: St. Martin's Press, Inc.

[XXII] Breslin, S. (2011, October 6). Why crazy people make better bloggers. Forbes. Retrieved from http://www.forbes.com/sites/susannahbreslin/2011/10/06/why-crazy-people-make-better-bloggers

[XXII] National Center for Health Statistics. (2006). Diagnosed attention deficit hyperactivity disorder and learning disability:

United States, 2004–2006. (DHHS Publication No. 2008–1565). Washington DC: U.S. Government Printing Office.

[XXIV] Carson, S. (2010) Your creative brain: Seven steps to maximize imagination, productivity, and innovation in your life. San Francisco, CA: Jossey-Bass.

[XXV] de Manzano, Ö., Cervenka, S., Karabanov. A., Farde, L., & Ullén, F. (2010). Thinking outside a less intact box: Thalamic dopamine D2 receptor densities are negatively related to psychometric creativity in healthy individuals. PLoS ONE, 5(5): e10670. doi:10.1371/journal.pone.0010670

[XXVI] Andrews, P.W., & Thomson Jr., A.W. (2009, July). The bright side of being blue: Depression as an adaptation for analyzing complex problems. Psychol Rev, 116(3), 620–654.

[XXVII] Gino, F., Sharek, Z., & Moore, D.A. (2011, March). Keeping the illusion of control under control: Ceilings, floors, and imperfect calibration. Organizational Behavior and Human Decision Processes, 114(2), 104–114.

[XXVIII] Rare nerve disorder leaves girl pain-free: Condition results in numerous injuries. Retrieved April 21, 2012, from http://www.msnbc.msn.com/id/4788525/ns/health-health_care/t/rare-nerve-disorder-leaves-girl-pain-free/#.T99wGHjFAso

[XXIX] Frankl, V. E. (1984). Man's search for meaning. New York, NY: Washington Square Press.

[XXX] Darley, J. M. & Gross, P. H. (1983). A hypothesis-confirming bias in labeling effects. Journal of Personality and Social Psychology, 44, 20-33.

[XXXI] Sedikides, C. & Strube, M. J. (1995). The multiply motivated self. Personality and Social Psychology Bulletin, 21(12), 1330–1335.

[XXXII] Thucydides (1950). The history of the Peloponnesian War. (R. Crawley, Trans.). New York, NY: E.P. Dutton and Co., Inc. (Original Work published n.d.)

[XXXIII] Tolstoy, L. (1899). What is art? (Alymer Maude, Trans.). Retrieved from http://archive.org/stream/whatisart00tolsuoft#page/n5/mode/2up

[XXXIV] Westen, D., Blagov, P. S., Harenski, K., Kilts, C. & Hamann, S. (2006). Neural bases of motivated reasoning: An fMRI study of emotional constraints on partisan political judgment in the 2004 U.S. presidential election. Journal of Cognitive Neuroscience, 18(11), 1947–1958.

[XXXV] Dan Gilbert asks, "Why are we happy?" [Video file]. (2004, February). Retrieved from http://www.ted.com/talks/view/lang/en//id/97

[XXXVI] Brehm, J. (1956). Post-decision changes in desirability of alternatives. Journal of Abnormal and Social Psychology, 52(3), 384–389.

[XXXVII] Stoner, J.A. (1961). A comparison of individual and group decision involving risk. (Unpublished master's thesis). Massachusetts Institute of Technology. Cambridge, MA.

[XXXVIII] Gordon, R., Franklin, N. & Beck, J. (2005). Wishful thinking and source monitoring. Memory & Cognition, 33(3), 418–429.

XXXIX Baird, F. E., & Kaufmann, W. (2008). From Plato to Derrida. Upper Saddle River, NJ: Pearson Prentice Hall.

XL Weinstein, N. D. (1980, November). Unrealistic optimism about future life events. Journal of Personality and Social Psychology. 39(5), 806-820.

XLI Kahneman, D. & Tversky, A. (1979). Prospect theory: An analysis of decision under risk. Econometrica, 47(2), 263-291.

XLII Johnson, S. (2010). Where good ideas come from: The natural history of innovation. New York, NY: Riverhead Books.

XLIII Newton, I. (1959). The correspondence of Isaac Newton, volume 1. (H.W. Turnbull, Ed.). Cambridge, MA: Cambridge University Press.

XLIV Ferguson, K. (2010 September) Everything is a Remix Part 1. [Video file]. Retrieved from http://www.everythingisaremix.info/watch-the-series/

Ferguson, K. (2011 February) Everything is a Remix Part 2. [Video file]. Retrieved from http://www.everythingisaremix.info/watch-the-series/

Ferguson, K. (2011 June) Everything is a Remix Part 3. [Video file]. Retrieved from http://www.everythingisaremix.info/watch-the-series/

Ferguson, K. (2012 February) Everything is a Remix Part 4. [Video file]. Retrieved from http://www.everythingisaremix.info/watch-the-series/

XLV U.S. Census Bureau. (2003). Educational attainment in the United States: 2003. [Data file]. Retrieved from http://www.census.gov/prod/2004pubs/p20-550.pdf

XLVI The Nielson Company. (2009). Average TV viewing per day. [Data file]. Retrieved from http://blog.nielsen.com/nielsenwire/media_entertainment/average-tv-viewing-for-2008-09-tv-season-at-all-time-high/

XLVII XPCT2WN. (2011, January 28). Jim Rohn-The law of average [Video file]. Retrieved from http://youtube/DMmz-_MLudQ

XLVIII Lencioni, P. (2002). The five dysfunctions of a team: A leadership fable. San Francisco, CA: Jossey-Bass.

XLIX Centre for Economic Performance. (2009, March). Does relative income matter? Are the critics right? London, ENG: Layard, R., Mayraz, G. & Nickell, S.

L Weiner, E. (2008). The geography of bliss: One grump's search for the happiest places in the world. New York, NY: Twelve.

LI Brickman, P., Coates, D. & Janoff-Bulman, R. (1978, August). Lottery winners and accident victims: Is happiness relative? Journal of Personality and Social Psychology, 36(8), 917-927.

LII Kahneman, D. & Deaton, A. (2010). High income improves evaluation of life but not emotional well-being. Proceedings of the National Academy of Sciences of the United States of America, 107(38), 16489-16493.

LIII Lykken, D. & Tellegen, A. (1996, May). Happiness is a stochastic phenomenon. University of Minnesota Psychological Science, 7(3), 186-189.

LIV Headey, B. (2008). Life goals matter to happiness: A revision of set-point theory. Social Indicators Research, 86(2), 213.

LV Dan Gilbert: The surprising science of happiness on TEDTALKS. [Video file]. (2004, February). Retrieved from http://www.ted.com/talks/dan_gilbert_asks_why_are_we_happy.html

LVI Ware, B. (2012). The top five regrets of the dying: A life transformed by the dearly departed. Retrieved from http://www.scribd.com/doc/88957383/Top-Five-Regrets-of-the-Dying-by-Bronnie-Ware-Excerpt

LVII Fincher, D. (Director). (1999). Fight Club. [Motion Picture]. United States, 20th Century Fox.

LVII Sandler, A. (1993). They're all gonna laugh at you. On They're all gonna laugh at you [D]. United States: Warner Brothers.

LIX Johnston, L. D., O'Malley, P. M., Bachman, J. G., & Schulenberg, J. E. (2011). Monitoring the future national survey results on drug use, 1975-2011. Volume I: Secondary school students. [Data file]. Retrieved from http://www.madd.org/statistics/

LX Fell, Jim. (1995). Repeat DWI offenders in the United States. [Data file]. Retrieved from http://www.madd.org/statistics/

LXI Federal Bureau of Investigation. (2010). Crime in the United States: 2010. Retrieved from http://www.madd.org/statistics/

LXII Domestic violence & substance abuse: Things you need to know. (2000). Retrieved April 5, 2012, from http://www.taadas.org/factsheets/DVFacts.htm

LXIII Children of alcoholics: Important facts. (1998). Retrieved March 15, 2012, from http://www.nacoa.net/impfacts.htm

LXIV World Health Organization. (2003). Adherence to long-term therapies: Evidence for action. Geneva, Switzerland: Sabaté, E.

LXV 60 percent doctors in China still smoke. (2010, April 26). In Thaindian News. Retrieved March 2, 2012, from http://www.thaindian.com/newsportal/health1/60-percent-doctors-in-china-still-smoke_100354411.html

LXVI World Health Organization. (2003). Adherence to long-term therapies: Evidence for action. Geneva, Switzerland: Sabaté, E.

LXVII Boone, C., de Brabander, B. & van Witteloostuijn, A. (1996, September). CEO locus of control and small firm performance: An integrative framework and empirical test. Journal of Management Studies, 33(5), 667-699.

LXVIII Collins, J. C. (2001). Good to great: Why some companies make the leap--and others don't. New York, NY: HarperBusiness.

LXIX Mill, J. (1909-14). Autobiography. C. W. Eliot (Ed.). New York, NY: P.F. Collier & Son.

LXX Gladwell, M. (2008). Outliers: The story of success. New York, NY: Little Brown and Co.

WA